THE CHARLTON
STANDARD CATALOGUE O

COALPORT
COLLECTABLES

FIRST EDITION

BY
ALF WILLIS

INTRODUCTION
BY
GAYE BLAKE ROBERTS

JEAN DALE
PUBLISHER

The Charlton Press

TORONTO, ONTARIO • PALM HARBOR, FLORIDA

Canadian Cataloguing in Publication Data

The National Library of Canada has catalogued this publication as follows:

The Charlton standard catalogue of Coalport collectables

Biennial
1st ed.-
ISSN 1492-3645
ISBN 0-88968-243-7 (2000 issue)

1. Figurines—England—Catalogs. 2. Coalport China Company—Catalogs. 3. Coalport porcelaine—Catalogs.

NK4399.C55C32   738.8'2'029442   C00-900593-5

Printed in Canada

EDITORIAL

Publisher and Editor	Jean Dale
Graphic Technician	Davina Rowan
Photography	David Hare, Neil Welch, Alf Willis

ACKNOWLEDGEMENTS

The Charlton Press and the author wish to thank those who have helped with the first edition of The Charlton Standard Catalogue of Coalport Collectables.

CONTRIBUTORS TO THE FIRST EDITION

The Publisher would like to thank the following individuals or companies who graciously supplied pricing, direct mail lists, photographs or allowed us access to their collections for photographic purposes. We offer our sincere thanks to:

Josiah Wedgwood & Sons Limited

Gaye Blake Roberts, Curator, Wedgwood Museum, and Museum Staff; Penny Brown, Curator, Ironbridge Museum Carol Baxendale-Potter; Jane Beeby; Les Challacombe; Roger Davies; Mark Fielding; Andy Flowers; Sam Jeffrey; Mike James; Natasha Hudson; Mike Peddar; Andrea Piddock; Peter Ross; Carol Rushton; Christine Smith; John Stecko; Tony Sullivan; Linda Taylor; Alan White; Lillian Willis; Stan Woodward, Customer Services, Wedgwood

Collectors

Maria Andreou, Fort Lee, NJ; Ann Burns, Antiquity Ann's Antiques, North Bay, ON; John Christopher, Mendota, IL; Mr. and Mrs. Len Field; Christine and Peter Grocock; Mr. and Mrs. Ray Hamblin; Jim and Susan Harron, A Moment in Time, Neptune, NJ; Anne Hughlett, I Spy Antiques, Gresham, OR; Carl Ihli, Bon Vivant Antiques and Period Furnishings, Annapolis, MD; Mimi and Steve Levine, Alexandria, VA; Steve and Judy Lipson, IL; Mark Lawson Antiques, Saratoga Springs, NY; Patricia Marsico and Jeanette Marsico, Mars-Most Antiques; Peter Ocala, FL; Mary Parris and John Fisher, Jomar Antiques, UK; Michael Sarbutts, UK; Mae Smith, Langley, BC; Lillian Stein, Tampa, FL

A SPECIAL NOTE TO COLLECTORS

We welcome and appreciate any comments or suggestions in regard to The Charlton Standard Catalogue of Coalport Collectables. If you would like to participate in pricing or supplying previously unavailable data or information, please contact Jean Dale at (416) 488-1418, or e-mail us at chpress@charltonpress.com.

A WORD ON BEHALF OF GAYE BLAKE ROBERTS
CURATOR OF THE WEDGWOOD MUSEUM

'As a Museum Curator, I am not licensed to comment on valuations for any purpose, not even that of insurance, and although I have provided historical assistance and information for this publication, I have had no association with the valuations indicated.'

The Charlton Press
Editorial Office
2040 Yonge Street, Suite 208, Toronto, Ontario. M4S 1Z9
Telephone: (416) 488-1418 Fax: (416) 488-4656
Telephone: (800) 442-6042 Fax: (800) 442-1542
www.charltonpress.com; e-mail: chpress@charltonpress.com

ALF WILLIS

Alf Willis was born in Burslem, Stoke-on-Trent in 1946. A family with a long tradition in the pottery industry, four generations, including his parents, were involved in this enterprise.

As a young boy, Alf would spend his free time at the Burslem School of Art where he remembers the distinctive smell of the oil paints and watching the artists at work. Throughout his school days his goal was to attend the Burslem School of Art. Unfortunately, this was impossible and at the age of fifteen Alf entered the pottery profession to make his living.

During his career he has worked for some of the major pottery manufacturers of the world. Alf commenced work for Coalport, a subsidiary of the Wedgwood Group, at the beginning of the 1990s. When he joined the company, he was only one of twenty figure painters. Today the number of painters has increased approximately eightfold.

A great portion of his working year consists of travelling both at home and abroad. He has made many appearances on both television and radio in England, Australia and Canada.

Alf lives with his wife Lillian and his two children in Stoke-on-Trent. His two sisters and one brother have also followed careers with the ceramic industry, ensuring that the Willis family tradition is kept alive.

It is not surprising to hear that Alf is enjoying his work today as much as when he first began over thirty years ago. He admits that he still experiences a feeling of excitement as each figurine is transformed from a blank canvas into a work of art, and is marked with the artist's monogram. His vast experience and skill are illustrated outwardly in his work, which has provided him with the prestigious and honoured title of Mastercraftsman, a distinction which cannot be disputed.

TABLE OF CONTENTS

HOW TO USE THIS CATALOGUE

THE LISTINGS

This book is designed to serve two specific purposes. First, to furnish the Coalport enthusiast with accurate listings containing vital information and photographs to aid in the building of a rewarding collection. Secondly, this publication provides Coalport collectors and dealers with current market prices for Coalport collectables.

Within the individual listings, the pieces are listed in alphabetical order. After the item's name comes **Designer**, the date of **Issue** and withdrawal, **Size, Colour**(s), and **Variations**. The **Series** to which the piece belongs (if applicable) is listed next. Lastly, the suggested retail **Price** is given in American, Canadian and British funds.

VARIETY CLASSIFICATIONS

Collectors will note the following distinction concerning styles and versions:

STYLES: When two or more models have the same name but different physical modelling characteristics, they are listed as **Style One, Style Two** and so on after their names.

VERSIONS: Versions are modifications to a major style element.

VARIATIONS: Variations are modifications to a minor style element. A change in colour is a variation.

A WORD ON PRICING

In addition to providing accurate information, this catalogue gives readers the most up-to-date retail prices for Coalport collectables in American, Canadian and British currencies.

To accomplish this, The Charlton Press continues to access an international pricing panel of Coalport experts that submits prices based on both dealer and collector retail-price activity, as well as current auction results. These market prices are carefully averaged to reflect accurate valuations in each of these three markets.

Please be aware that all prices given in a particular currency are for figures within that particular country. The prices published herein have not been calculated using exchange rates exclusively. They have been determined solely by supply and demand within the country in question.

A necessary word of caution. No pricing catalogue can be, or should be, a fixed price list. This catalogue, therefore, should be considered as a pricing guide only — showing the most current retail prices based on market demand within a particular region for the various items.

Current collectables, however, are priced differently in this catalogue. Such pieces are priced according to the manufacturer's suggested retail price in each of the three market regions. It should be noted that it is likely dealer discounting from these prices will occur.

One exception, however, occurs in the case of current models or recent limited editions issued in only one of the three markets. Since such items were priced by Coalport only in the country in which they were to be sold, prices for other markets are not shown.

The prices published herein are for pieces in mint condition. Collectors are cautioned that a repaired or restored piece may be worth as little as 25 per cent of the value of the same piece in mint condition. The collector interested strictly in investment potential will avoid damaged figurines.

THE INTERNET AND PRICING

The Internet is changing the way business is being done in the collectable marketplace. Linking millions of collectors around the world through chat rooms, antique and collector malls, Internet auctions and producer web sites, e-commerce has become big business.

Some of the effects caused by the Internet and e-commerce on the collectables business are as follows:

1. Collectors deal directly with other collectors, changing the dynamics of the traditional customer/dealer relationship.

2. Information concerning new issues, finds and varieties is readily available, twenty-four hours a day. Collectors' wants are made known instantly to a wide spectrum of dealers and collectors.

3. Prices:
   (a) Price differentials will disappear between global market areas as collectors and the delivery services team up to stretch the purchasing power of the collectable dollar/pound.
   (b) Prices of common to scarce items will adjust downward to compensate for the temporary expansion of merchandise supply. Conversely, prices of rare and extremely rare items will increase, a result of additional exposure to demand.
   (c) After a time even the prices of the common items will rise due to the growing worldwide demand for collectables.

4. Internet auction sites listing millions of items for sale on a daily basis continue to grow as more and more collectors discover the viability of using this method to buy and sell merchandise.

5. Traditional marketing strategies (retail stores, direct-mail retailers, collectable shows and fairs, and collectable magazines and papers) face increased pressure in a more competitive environment.

The Internet is user-friendly: no travelling required, twenty-four hour accessibility, no face-to-face contact or other pressure to buy or sell. Without a doubt, the arrival of e-commerce will change the way a collector adds to their collection.

INTRODUCTION
By Gaye Blake Roberts

A romantic ornament with a very practical function would best describe the cottages created by the Coalport Company in Shropshire. These pastille burners were produced in many architectural forms such as cottages, castles and churches and even industrial buildings. The earliest known English ceramic cottages date back to the middle of the 18th century when earthenware examples were produced, as money boxes or purely as ornaments, but porcelain examples were primarily manufactured between 1810 and 1850. There has however been a major resurgence of interest in these charming objects in the second half of the 20th century.

Initially pastille burners, in the form of cottages, were made in an age when the hygiene in houses was not as good as today and unpleasant smells were common. In both Georgian and Victorian England, when gracious living was a practised art, even the noblest home faced the problem of bad odours. Each room was supplied with aromatic herbs placed in pot pourri bowls or contained within embroidered sachets. The wealthy even employed servants whose particular task was to carry, from room to room, perfuming pans in which were placed burning sweet smelling herbs. It is possible that this is the origin of the practice that eventually led to the more practical solution of each room permanently housing a container in which to burn the perfumed oils and herbs. The earliest references to pastille burners date back to Elizabethan times when the vessels were manufactured from silver but by the early 18th century pastille burners were frequently referred to as cassolettes, defined in 1726 as 'small Vessels for the Burning of Pastils (sic) and other odours'.

The concept of cottages as pastille burners coincided with the golden age of Bone China production and they began to be manufactured at a time when objects were collected as ornaments, something which became particularly prevalent during the Victorian era. Houses became increasingly filled with objets d'art placed on every available surface as seen in the surviving illustrations of interiors of the period. Aromatic pastilles were placed inside the burners and when lit emitted a pleasant aroma, the aromatic smoke appropriately curling upwards through the chimney in a naturalistic way. As late as 1850 Theodore Hook wrote of placing 'three or four pastilles into the burner on the mantelpiece' which were designed to burn slowly, inside the ceramic building, providing a pleasant atmosphere for many hours at a time.

Cottage pastille burners were frequently made in two sections either with the roof and walls shaped as a single piece to cover a flat plinth on which the pastille burned, or more rarely so that the roof could be lifted off serving as a removable lid. Sometimes the piece was manufactured with a large hole in at the back to enable the pastille to be placed inside the building. The actual pastilles, which were cone shaped, were made to traditional recipes. Three types were particularly popular, they were à la rose, orange-flower and vanilla. However, violets, jasmine or sandalwood were also frequently used in place of the roses which seem to have been the most popular.

The ingredients for a rose pastille would have consisted of a charcoal powder, gum benzoin, olibanum (frankincense) and storax (all aromatic resins), nitre and essence of roses (or powder of pale roses). All the ingredients were then mixed with rosewater, gum tragacanth and the resultant paste was shaped into cones.

The popularity of these pastille burners really reached its peak in the first half of the 19th century but with improved hygiene and changing taste and fashions the burner steadily became less well modelled and quality production faded out by 1850. During the first half of the 19th century, most of the celebrated and important English manufacturers produced cottages, including the factories of Worcester, Minton, Derby, Spode, Samuel Alcock and many unidentified Staffordshire Bone China manufacturers as well as Coalport. The majority were near-rectangular in plan, but circular and hexagonal and even irregular shapes are known. It is interesting that recent research into this subject has led to the re-attribution of many of the old Coalport cottages and it is now thought that they made far fewer models than was previously assumed, which makes the surviving marked examples so much rarer.

The choice of location of the Coalport Works, in Shropshire, was almost certainly dictated by its waterside location, providing excellent transport facilities for the delivery of raw materials and the dispatch of finished goods either upstream to Shrewsbury, the county town, or downstream to Stourport for transhipment onto the national canal system (the canals of Shropshire were not connected directly into the national system until the middle of the 19th century), to the port of Bristol and beyond to the known world.

The original partners of the Coalport manufactory, John Rose and Edward Blakeway, established a new brick-built factory, on the land leased in 1795. It was a long, narrow construction, with a three storied building located at each end, one of which contained a kiln. It is possible that the actual construction work was undertaken by local builders Samuel and William Smith of Madeley, a nearby market town, to a design and layout agreed upon with Rose and Blakeway. The land on which the new factory was constructed was quite steeply sloping, as is normal on the valley side, so that on one side the lowest floor opened onto the canal bank, whilst on the other side of the building the 'first floor' opened directly onto Coalport High Street. Sadly, there are very few contemporary descriptions of the pot bank, however, one written in 1859 by the historian and ceramist, John Randall described the scene from the top of the valley as 'a landscape not unpleasing - we ought, perhaps, to say when not obscured by smoke ... the grim-looking factory, its bottle shaped ovens, its white china heaps, its black smoke columns. Above the works a little ferry plying from side to side with toil-freed artisans, hastening to meals, or answering the brazen summons of the bell to renew their labour.'

One of the most productive periods of production at Coalport dates from 1815 with John's acquisition of his brother's factory which was adjacent to his own, built between the canal and the river and which when the two sites were united provided a very strong manufacturing basis. Rose was already assured of his local market and had established a considerable presence in London. Possibly one of John Rose's most notable achievements

Based on Coalport's original 19th-century mould, the ornate 'Umbrella House' was reintroduced in 1964.

occurred during this period when he successfully perfected a leadless feldspathic glaze for which he was awarded a gold medal by the Society of Arts (later the Royal Society of Arts). The widespread use of lead within the ceramic industry, both as a vital ingredient of porcelain and as a flux in the glaze, had given considerable concern. Rose made enormous capital from the award, made on the 30th May 1820, by creating an impressive mark. It is fair to state that Rose dominated much of the ceramic industry in the early years of the 19th century, with the factory going from strength to strength. He was renowned for employing a number of highly talented artists who created some of the most beautiful designs at this period.

Some of the early marked Coalport cottages included a gazebo, with all the flamboyance of a garden folly, a stylised church and a simple rustic cottage. The early pastille burners are sometimes marked with the script 'CD' factory mark, an abbreviation of the name Coalbrookdale, which refers to the area in Shropshire in which the Coalport manufactory was located. It is now thought, however, that

in the first half of the 19th century Coalport only made four or five different models at the most.

In 1825, the self-consuming candlewick was invented, and as a result many of the china cottages began to be used as night lights with the faint rays of illumination coming through the doors and windows. This however was the exception rather than general practice.

John Rose died in 1841 leaving the legacy of a factory, which not only bore his name, but which he had developed to manufacture a range of fine wares, produced under his direction, for posterity and as a lasting memorial to his inspiration and hard work, not least of which were the early models of cottage pastille burners. The works continued to be managed by a succession of partners including Thomas Rose (until 1843), Charles Maddison, William Pugh and W.F. Rose until 1875 when Pugh died and the works were placed under the control of Chancery prior to a receiver being appointed to continue production at the factory. The

'Thatched Cottage', second version, with a removable lid.

Coalport factory was sold, in 1881, to Peter Schuyler Bruff, an engineer from East Anglia. Eight years later his son, Charles Bruff, became the managing director and renamed the firm the Coalport China Company.

The improvements made by Bruff are recorded in an article describing, 'A Brief Visit to Coalport', which appeared in the Pottery Gazette of October 1906, it reads; 'the works have been greatly enlarged and a considerable portion of them have been rebuilt, and new and improved machinery and appliances have been introduced.... Every provision seems to have been made for the health, convenience, and comfort of the employees. The artists and decorators work under the most pleasant conditions. Light and well ventilated rooms look over the River Severn to the wooded scenery on the opposite banks. There are about 300 employed altogether....The ancient and modern mingle at Coalport in the most harmonious fashion.'

In 1925 the Coalport China Company Limited was sold to Cauldon Potteries Limited of North Staffordshire and one year later the original factory in Shropshire closed with all aspects of production, unfinished ware and stock and many of the employees transferring to 'The Potteries' in Staffordshire to work. Tradition in the Coalport factory and amongst the employees always suggested that it was fortunate that some of the original models for the cottage pastille burners had survived within the factory and were brought to Staffordshire in 1926. As has already been indicated this would not have been a significant number and it is impossible to prove whether any of the original early moulds actually survived. It is far more probable that a few original models may have been transferred.

In 1963 under the direction of Mr. Brain, of E. Brain and Company, the then owner of the Coalport factory who had acquired the works in 1958, it was decided to re-introduce six pastille burners, which were to be faithful reproductions of old examples, initially the models released were; the Thatched Cottage, Park Lodge, Parasol House, Summer House, Umbrella House and The Castle (Style One). These were launched at the International Gift Fair at Blackpool a year later in 1964. This decision marked the start of an international renaissance and interest in these pieces. Since then the range has been steadily increased, each piece having its own charm and attraction.

The manufacture of a Coalport cottage is today almost identical to the way it would have been produced nearly two hundred years ago. The first requirement is an image of the building, whether in the past an engraving or drawing or today a photograph. The method used by the company in recent times is to produce the first model in plaster of Paris. The modeller prepares a smooth plaster slab, or 'bat' and then outlines first in pencil then with a sharp tool, the shape of each wall of the cottage, the roof and the base. Once he is satisfied with the form, he then engraves the fine details, such as the doors, windows, architectural detail together with any textures such as the bricks and stone, onto each piece. From this original plaster bat a mould is taken, which preserves all the details, but reverses them, so that the incised lines now stand proud of the surrounding plaster. The mould is then used to make an impression in a slab of clay which corresponds with the original plaster bat. Each section of the cottage is cut out and assembled to form a complete clay model. This clay model is then passed to the mould maker, whose job is to produce a master mould of the cottage from which the subsequent working moulds will be taken. The mould may be in several parts, according to the complexity of the individual cottage. Once the separate sections of the cottage have been cast from the mould they have to be assembled by hand whilst the clay is still moist. Rough edges are smoothed away and any additional decoration, in the form of handmade flowers or shredded clay to resemble moss, is applied.

The model is left to dry before being fired for the first time into the 'biscuit' state. Any underglaze colours are added prior to the cottage being dipped into a liquid glaze and fired for the second time. The final decorative details are added, together with any gilding, before the piece receives its final firing at a lower temperature to fuse the colours into the glaze.

Many special commissions have been produced for both the home and overseas markets and includes subjects made especially for specialist retailers including, Old North Church, Boston as an edition of fifty for Shreve Crump and Lowe of America in 1973 and many other named individual buildings for the Peter Jones, Mulberry Hall and John Sinclair shops as well as replicas of properties owned by the National Trust, including The Clergy House, Alfriston and Blaise Hamlet Cottage. For The Ironbridge Gorge Museum an actual copy of the Coalport China works was manufactured entitled 'Bottle Oven' which was made in 1983. A more detailed description of these unusual and interesting specimens are included in the text of this

Old North Church

volume. Many of the 20th century cottages are based on recognisable buildings such as the Village School which is adapted from the school in Barlaston Village, whilst the Country Railway Station is based on Stone Station, and the Christmas Church that of Swynnerton, all in the county of Staffordshire. The range of cottages and their inspiration is almost endless with some taken from literature, others from abroad, and many replicas and adaptations of the diverse styles of English architecture.

The functional qualities of the early cottages as pastille burners has grown into a popular aesthetic object for the home offering historical interest through the representations of English architecture over the decades. Coalport cottages prove to be lasting mementoes of the years gone-by and will always be a welcome addition into any collection.

Gaye Blake Roberts

HOW TO COLLECT COALPORT COLLECTABLES

A Coalport collection may begin from a variety of sources. A chance gift, a souvenir picked up on holiday, or an appreciation of Coalport craftsmanship can initiate a lifetime of extremely satisfying collecting. It is not unusual for very large collections to be created in a comparatively short time as one's enthusiasm rises.

For those aspiring to form a complete collection, it is advisable to keep up with all the current introductions, as they can become very elusive once discontinued. Those searching for that special piece sometimes face stiff competition, not to mention sky-high prices. Fortunately, today's collectors have a number of options when developing their collections. Auction houses and antique fairs are both excellent sources for collectors. Estate auctions are another area to explore, as are specialist dealers. The Internet can be an invaluable tool for purchasing items, as well as gathering information on a specific piece.

Rather than purchasing every Coalport collectable item available, it is wise to decide at the beginning exactly what type of collection you wish to develop. Collections are often based on one of four criteria: series, subject, size, or artist.

Collecting by Series

Many collectors prefer this traditional approach to collecting. Cottage admirers could start to accumulate the Collectors Cottages, Derbyshire Well Dressings, English Barns, Historical Buildings of Yorkshire, Miniature Cottages or the Pastille Burners series. Additionally, the Alice in Wonderland, Children's Collection, Cinderella, Egg Boxes, Little Grey Rabbit, Paddington Bear, Postman Pat, Royal Commemoratives or Sleeping Beauty series are all excellent places to start building a collection.

Collecting by Subject

Collecting by subject or theme, independent of series, is also quite common. This could result in a collection by type of building (i.e. churches), by region, or of commemorative pieces (i.e. the Anniversary Cottage) which were under limited release.

If several colourways, versions or variations of a single piece exist, a collector may also choose to gather all of these models.

Collecting by Size

Acquiring pieces of a particular size may appeal to a collector. Cottages range in size: for example, the Toadstool Cottage is 5 ¾" while the Village Inn is only 2" high. Dimensions of Coalport figurines, miniature tableware and novelties also vary.

Collecting by Artist

The work of a specific designer or modeller such as Catherine Barnsely, Sue McGarrigle or Arnold Woolam may interest a collector.

Care and Repair

A Coalport collection can be enjoyed indefinitely as long as care is taken when handling and cleaning. When dusting in situ, a soft cosmetic brush or photographic lens brush is useful for getting into tight corners, particularly the hand-modelled flowers which adorn many of the cottages. When necessary, glazed pieces should be washed in luke-warm water, using a mild liquid detergent, then rinsed thoroughly and dried naturally or buffed gently with a soft cloth. It is important that water does not get inside: if there is a hole in the bottom, it should be blocked up beforehand, perhaps with a cork or a rubber bung. Care should be taken not to knock models against the tap or against each other, as this may cause chips or imperceptible cracks in the glaze which could upen up at a later date.

If the worst happens, a professional restorer should be consulted as they can work 'miracles' with damaged pieces. Whether it be a small chip or a shattered cottage, pieces can be mended so that the repair is invisible to all but the most experienced eye. It follows that when buying pieces on the secondary market, it is advisable to check for restorations. Projecting details are the most vulnerable parts, so look at these areas carefully in a good light. Repaired cracks can sometimes be detected by looking inside the piece through the hole in the bottom. There are special ultraviolet lamps which highlight some types of restoration but these are not widely used, except by professionals. Restored models should be priced less than perfect examples, according to the amount of damage and the quality of the repair. Always enquire about the condition of a piece when buying, as a reputable dealer will stand by any guarantees they give regarding restorations.

Insuring Your Collectables

As with any other valuables, making certain your collectables are protected is a very important concern. It is paramount that you display or store any porcelain items in a secure place, preferably one safely away from traffic in the home.

Your collectables are most often covered under your basic homeowner's policy. There are generally three kinds of such policies: standard, broad and comprehensive. Each has its own specific deductible and terms.

Under a general policy, your collectables are considered contents and are covered for all of the perils listed under the contractual terms of your policy (fire, theft, water damage and so on).

However, since collectables are extremely delicate, breakage is treated differently by most insurance companies. There is usually an extra premium attached to insure collectables against accidental breakage by or carelessness of the owner. This is sometimes referred to as a fine arts rider.

You are advised to contact your insurance professional to get all the answers.

In order to help protect your collection, it is critical that you take inventory of your collectables and have colour photographs taken of all your pieces. This is the surest method of establishing clearly, for the police and your insurance company, the items lost or destroyed. It is also the easiest way to establish their replacement value in the event of a tragedy.

A GUIDE TO BACKSTAMPS

Over the years, many different backstamps have been found on Coalport items. Most of the early models (before 1880) carrying the first stamps are extremely rare, and are beyond the scope of this guide. The period we are concerned with is 1880 to date. The following table illustrates the chronological order of Coalport backstamps for this period.

Please remember that this is only our third attempt at constructing a backstamp dating system. More research is needed to make this a definitive guide for backstamps, and collectors are advised that this listing may contain errors. If you can help to clarify backstamp chronology, please contact Jean Dale, 2040 Yonge Street, Suite. 208, Toronto, Ontario, M4S 1Z9, Canada, (416) 488-1418.

CROWN - 1880 - 1891
(Usually green in colour)

MADE IN ENGLAND CROWN - 1915 - 1949
(May range in colour from green to black to gold)

ENGLAND CROWN - 1891 - 1915
(Usually green in colour)

1949 - 1958
(May range in colour from blue to orange)

1958-1973

1986 - 1993

Fine Bone China

1973 - 1985

Bone China

Bone China

1994 TO DATE

Bone China

Porcelain

Porcelain

COALPORT

Josiah Wedgwood & Sons Limited
Barlaston
Stoke-on-Trent, ST12 9ES
England
Tel.: +44 (0) 1782 204141
Fax: +44 (0) 1782 204222
www.wedgwood.com

Waterford-Wedgwood Canada Inc.
20 West Beaver Creek Road
Richmond Hill, Ontario L4B 3L6
Canada
Tel.: +1 (905) 886-6400
Fax: +1 (905) 886-6532

Waterford-Wedgwood USA Inc.
41 Madison Avenue, 23rd Floor
New York, N.Y. 10010
U.S.A.
Tel.: +1 (800) 955-1550
Fax: +1 (908) 938-6915
www.wedgwood-usa.com

COALPORT COLLECTOR SOCIETY

In 1994, a Coalport Collector Society was formed. The annual membership entitles members to a magazine published quarterly, a complimentary figurine, and factory visits. As well, Coalport produces special edition figurines, which are only available to club members. For information on joining the Society, contact the address below:

Coalport Collector Society
P.O. Box 99
Sudbury, Suffolk CO10 6SN
England

Waterford-Wedgwood Canada Inc.
20 West Beaver Creek Road
Richmond Hill, Ontario L4B 3L6
Canada
Attn.: Coalport Collector Society

THE WEDGWOOD STORY
(The World's Finest Factory Tour)

The Wedgwood Story is open every day of the year except for Christmas week and New Year's Day.
Opening times: Monday to Friday 9am to 5pm; Saturday 10am to 5pm; Sunday 10am to 5pm (shop closes at 4pm)
For more information or ticket prices, telephone or write: The Wedgwood Story, Barlaston, Stoke-on-Trent ST12 9ES,
Tel.: +44 (0) 1782 204218, www.thewedgwoodstory.com

OTHER PLACES TO VISIT

The Coalport China Museum
Ironbridge Gorge Museum
Ironbridge, Shropshire TF8 7AW
England
Tel.: +44 (0) 1952 580650
Fax: +44 (0) 1952 432204

Wedgwood Factory Shop
Sidings Place
King Street
Fenton, Stoke-on-Trent ST4 3DQ
England
Tel.: +44 (0) 1782 316161

Discontinued Coalport collectables can be found in antique shops, markets, auctions, shows and fairs. Specialist delaers in Coalport attend many of the events listed below.

For auction happenings it is necessary to subscribe to Auction Houses that hold 20th Century Auctions.

UNITED KINGDOM
Land-based Auction Houses

Bonhams
65-69 Lots Road, Chelsea
London SW10 ORN, England
Tel.: +44 (0207) 393 3900
Fax: +44 (0207) 393 3906
www.bonhams.com
Attn.: Neil Grenyer

Christie's South Kensington
85 Old Brompton Road
London SW7 3LD, England
Tel.: +44 (0207) 5817611
Fax: +44 (0207) 321-3321
www.christies.com
Attn.: Michael Jeffrey

Potteries Specialist Auctions
271 Waterloo Road
Stoke-on-Trent ST6 3HR
Staffordshire, England
Tel.: +44 (0) 1782 286622
Fax: +44 (0) 1782 213777
Attn.: Steve Anderson

Louis Taylor
Britannia House
10 Town Road, Hanley
Stoke-on-Trent ST1 2QG, England
Tel.: +44 (0) 1782 214111
Fax.: +44 (0) 1782 215283
Attn.: Clive Hillier

Phillips
101 New Bond Street
London W1Y OAS, England
Tel.: +44 (0207) 629 6602
Fax: +44 (0207) 629 8876
www.phillips-auctions.com
Attn.: Mark Oliver

Sotheby's
34-35 New Bond Street
London W1A 2AA, England
Tel.: +44 (0207) 293 5000
Fax: +44 (0207) 293 5989
www.sothebys.com
Attn: Christina Donaldson

Sotheby's Sussex
Summers Place
Billinghurst, Sussex RH14 9AF
England
Tel.: +44 (0) 1403 833500
Fax: +44 (0) 1403 833699

Thomson Roddick & Laurie
60 Whitesands
Dumfries DG1 2RS, Scotland
Tel.: +44 (0) 1387 255366
Fax: +44 (0) 1387 266236
Attn.: Sybelle Medcalf

Peter Wilson Auctioneers
Victoria Gallery, Market Street
Nantwich, Cheshire CW5 5DG
England
Tel.: +44 (0) 1270 623878
Fax: +44 (0) 1270 610508
Attn.: Stella Ashbrook or
        Robert Stone

Antique Markets

Alfie's Antique Market
13-25 Church Street
London
Tuesday - Saturday

Camden Passage Market
London
Wednesday and Saturday

New Caledonia Market
Bermondsey Square, London
Friday morning

Portobello Market
Portbello Road
London
Saturday

UNITED STATES
Land-based Auction Houses

Bonhams
c/o William Doyle Galleries
175 East 87th Street
New York, NY 10128
Tel.: (212) 427-2730
Fax: (212) 369-0892

Christie's East
219 East 67th Street
New York, NY 10021
Tel.: (212) 606-0400
www.christies.com
Attn.: Timothy Luke

Sotheby's Arcade Auctions
1334 York Avenue
New York, NY 10021
Tel.: (212) 606-7000
www.sothebys.com
Attn.: Andrew Cheney

Collectable Shows

Atlantique City
New Atlantic City Convention Center
Atlantic City, New Jersey
Usually March and October
For information on times and dates:
Brimfield and Associates
P.O. Box 1800, Ocean City, NJ 08226
Tel.: (609) 926-1800
www.atlantiquecity.com

O'Hare National Antiques Show & Sale
Rosemont Convention Center, Chicago, Illinois
Usually April, August and November
For information on times and dates:
Manor House Shows Inc.
P.O. Box 7320, Fort Lauderdale, FL 33338
Tel.: (954) 563-6747

CANADA
Land-based Auction Houses

Maynards
415 West 2nd Avenue
Vancouver, B.C. V5Y 1E3
Tel.: (604) 876-1311

Ritchie's
288 King Street East
Toronto, Ontario M5A 1K4
Tel.: (416) 364-1864 Fax: (416) 364-0704
Attn.: Caroline Kaiser

Collectables Shows

Canadian Art & Collectible Show & Sale
Kitchener Memorial Auditorium
Kitchener, Ontario
Usually early May
For information on times and location:
George or Jackie Benninger
P.O. Box 130, Durham, Ontario, N0G 1R0
Tel.: (519) 369-6950

Canadian Doulton & Collectable Fair
Toronto, Ontario
Usually early September
For information on times and location:
George or Jackie Benninger
P.O. Box 130, Durham, Ontario, N0G 1R0
Tel.: (519) 369-6950

INTERNET SITES

Auction Sites

http://www.amazon.com/
http://www.auctions.com/
http://www.Auctions-on-line.com/
http://www.ebay.com/
http://auctions.excite.com/
http://auctions.lycos.com/
http://auctions.shopping.com/
http://auctions.xoom.com/
http://auctions.yahoo.com/

Antique Mall Sites

http://www.icollector.co.uk.com/
http://www.tias.com/
htto://www.worldcollectorsnet.com

The Charlton Press does not endorse any of these sites,
they are listed for convenience only.

THE VILLA

COTTAGES

BELVEDERE

THE ALMS HOUSES

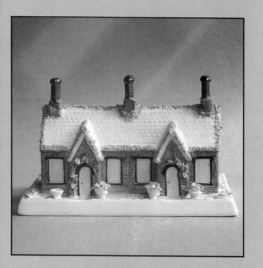

THE ALMS HOUSES

TECHNICAL DATA

Designer:	Tony Sims
Modeller:	Tony Sims
Height:	3 ½", 8.9 cm
Colour:	Brown walls and chimneys; white roof; pale yellow windows; deeper yellow doors; green decoration
Issued:	1983-1989

PRICING DATA

U.S.	$200.00
Can.	$275.00
U.K.	£150.00

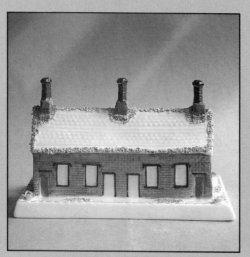

Top: Front veiw
Bottom: Back view

THE AMERICAN CHURCH

The American Church
by
Coalport
Fine Bone China
Made in England

THE AMERICAN CHURCH

TECHNICAL DATA

Designer:	Arnold Woolam
Modeller:	Arnold Woolam
Height:	8 ½", 21.6 cm
Colour:	White; brown clock dial; red, blue, pink and purple flowers; green leaves
Issued:	1976-1980

PRICING DATA

U.S.	$600.00
Can.	$875.00
U.K.	£400.00

Top: Front view
Centre: Back view
Bottom: Side view

ANNE HATHAWAY'S COTTAGE

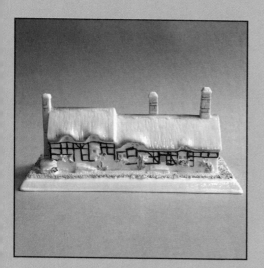

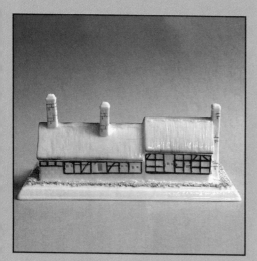

> Anne Hathaway's Cottage.
> Shottery, Stratford-upon-Avon.
> The picturesque thatched home of
> Anne Hathaway before her marriage to
> Shakespeare is preserved as a
> national memorial by the
> Shakespeare Birthplace Trust.
> by
> Coalport
> Fine Bone China
> Made in England

ANNE HATHAWAY'S COTTAGE
Shottery, Stratford-upon-Avon

TECHNICAL DATA

Designer:	Arnold Woolam
Modeller:	Arnold Woolam
Height:	2 ½", 5.7 cm
Colour:	Cream walls; black beams; yellow and brown roof; pink, blue and yellow flowers; green grass and trim
Issued:	1981-1984

PRICING DATA

U.S.	$175.00
Can.	$250.00
U.K.	£125.00

Top: Front view
Bottom: Back view

ANNIVERSARY COTTAGE

This cottage, with a removable top, was issued to commemorate the 250th Anniversary of Coalport 1750-2000.

Backstamp not available at press time

ANNIVERSARY COTTAGE

TECHNICAL DATA

Designer:	Sue McGarrigle
Modeller:	Jenny Oliver
Height:	5", 12.7 cm
Colour:	White; pale green roof; green moss; pink doors; gold-edged roof and windows
Issued:	2000 in a limited edition of 1,750
Series:	250th Anniversary of Coalport

PRICING DATA

U.S.	$ —
Can.	$ —
U.K.	£135.00

Top: Front view
Centre: Back view
Bottom: Side view

THE ARBOUR

Surrounded and supported by slender tree trunks, this golden-roofed little cottage spins its own web of magic and mystery.

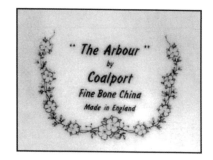

" The Arbour "
by
Coalport
Fine Bone China
Made in England

THE ARBOUR

TECHNICAL DATA

Designer:	Andrew Bill
Modeller:	Andrew Bill
Height:	3 ¾", 9.5 cm
Colour:	White, yellow and brown roof and trees; green decoration
Issued:	1988-1990
Series:	Pastille Burners

PRICING DATA

U.S.	$200.00
Can.	$275.00
U.K.	£150.00

Top: Front view
Centre: Back view
Bottom: Side view

ASHFORD IN THE WATER WELL

This model was commissioned by Sinclairs in a limited edition of 500 pieces.

Backstamp not
available
at press time

ASHFORD IN THE WATER WELL

TECHNICAL DATA

Designer:	Arnold Woolam
Modeller:	Arnold Woolam
Height:	3 ¾", 9.5 cm
Colour:	Red roof with decorative panel; multicoloured scene of St. George slaying the dragon
Issued:	1983 in a limited edition of 500
Series:	Derbyshire Well Dressings

PRICING DATA

U.S.	$250.00
Can.	$350.00
U.K.	£175.00

Top: Front view

"BANK BARN" LAKE DISTRICT

"BANK BARN" LAKE DISTRICT

TECHNICAL DATA

Designer:	Andrew Bill
Modeller:	Andrew Bill
Height:	2 ½", 5.7 cm
Colour:	Grey walls; pink-yellow roof; dark green tree and trim; dark brown door and windows; white base
Issued:	1987-1988
Series:	English Barns

PRICING DATA

U.S.	$125.00
Can.	$175.00
U.K.	£90.00

Top: Front view
Centre: Back view
Bottom: Side view

BARLEY SUGAR HOUSE

This fantasy cottage with its barley twist columns and three blue roofs is based on an original pastille burner.

BARLEY SUGAR HOUSE

TECHNICAL DATA

Designer:	Andrew Bill
Modeller:	Andrew Bill
Height:	4 ½", 11.9 cm
Colour:	White; blue roofs; yellow columns; brown door; gold window and door frames
Issued:	1987-1990
Variation:	Fortune Towers
Series:	Pastille Burners

PRICING DATA

U.S.	$200.00
Can.	$275.00
U.K.	£150.00

Top: Front view
Bottom: Back view

THE BELL TOWER

The intricate lines of 'The Bell Tower' hint at a highly complex network of rooms beneath the blue-roofed towers.

THE BELL TOWER

TECHNICAL DATA

Designer:	Andrew Bill
Modeller:	Andrew Bill
Height:	4 ¾", 12.1 cm
Colour:	White; turquoise and pale blue roof; gold window frames; purple and yellow decoration
Issued:	1988-1990
Variation:	Summer Palace
Series:	Pastille Burners

PRICING DATA

U.S.	$200.00
Can.	$275.00
U.K.	£150.00

Top: Front view
Bottom: Back view

BELVEDERE

The first of a series of Collectors' Cottages, the Belvedere is a new design based on an antique cottage. Today's Belvedere has a gilded dove, more intricate detail in the wall embossing, and has been hand-painted using richer Imari colours. Issued in a limited edition of 500, this cottage comes boxed with a certificate of authenticity.

BELVEDERE

TECHNICAL DATA

Designer:	Andrew Bill
Modeller:	Andrew Bill
Height:	6 ¼", 15.9 cm
Colour:	White; blue roof; brown doors and chimneys; brown vines; brown and blue roses.
Issued:	1988 in a limited edition of 500
Series:	Collectors' Cottages

PRICING DATA

U.S.	$325.00
Can.	$475.00
U.K.	£225.00

Top: Front view
Centre: Back view

THE BERMUDA COTTAGE

THE BERMUDA COTTAGE

TECHNICAL DATA

Designer:	Arnold Woolam
Modeller:	Arnold Woolam
Height:	3 ¾", 9.5 cm
Colour:	Pink walls; white roof and fence; green shutters and door
Issued:	1979-1982

PRICING DATA

U.S.	$175.00
Can.	$250.00
U.K.	£125.00

Top: Front view
Centre: Back view
Bottom: Side view

BERMUDA LIGHTHOUSE

Backstamp not
available
at press time

BERMUDA LIGHTHOUSE
St. David's

TECHNICAL DATA

Designer:	Tony Sims
Modeller:	Tony Sims
Height:	6 ¼", 15.9 cm
Colour:	Brown cottage, white roof; white lighthouse with red band; green moss
Issued:	1983-1988
Variation:	Lighthouse

PRICING DATA

U.S.	$250.00
Can.	$350.00
U.K.	£175.00

Top: Front view
Bottom: Back view

BIRTHPLACE OF CAPTAIN JAMES COOK

This cottage was commissioned by Lewis and Cooper, North Allerton, in a limited edition of 300.

Backstamp not
available
at press time

BIRTHPLACE OF CAPTAIN JAMES COOK

TECHNICAL DATA

Designer:	Tony Sims
Modeller:	Tony Sims
Height:	2 ¾", 7.0 cm
Colour:	White; yellow roof; brown boat
Issued:	1983 in a limited edition of 300

PRICING DATA

U.S.	$300.00
Can.	$450.00
U.K.	£200.00

Top: Front view
Centre: Back view
Bottom: Side view

BLAISE HAMLET

This limited edition cottage was commissioned by the National Trust.

> Backstamp not
> available
> at press time

BLAISE HAMLET

TECHNICAL DATA

Designer:	Andrew Bill
Modeller:	Andrew Bill
Height:	3 ½", 8.9 cm
Colour:	Beige walls; brownish-yellow roof; yellow verandah; green moss
Issued:	1987 in a limited edition
Series:	Pastille Burners

PRICING DATA

U.S.	$200.00
Can.	$275.00
U.K.	£150.00

Top: Front view
Bottom: Side view

THE BLUE HOUSE

The Blue House
by
Coalport
Fine Bone China
Made in England

THE BLUE HOUSE

TECHNICAL DATA

Designer:	Arnold Woolam
Modeller:	Arnold Woolam
Height:	4 ¾", 12.1 cm
Colour:	White; dark blue roof; red chimney and door; dark brown door and window frames; light brown steps; pink, blue and yellow flowers; green moss
Issued:	1980-1983

PRICING DATA

U.S.	$200.00
Can.	$275.00
U.K.	£150.00

Top: Front view

THE BOTTLE OVEN

The Bottle Oven
Coalport China Works
Shropshire
by
Coalport
Fine Bone China
Made in England

THE BOTTLE OVEN

TECHNICAL DATA

Designer:	Tony Sims
Modeller:	Tony Sims
Height:	4", 10.1 cm
Colour:	Light brown walls; brown door; white roof; pink and blue flowers; green tree and moss
Issued:	1983-1984

PRICING DATA

U.S.	$250.00
Can.	$350.00
U.K.	£175.00

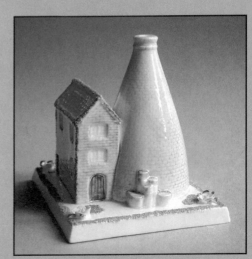

Top: Front view
Centre: Back view
Bottom: Side view

THE BOWER

This cottage is based on an antique pastille burner. 'The Bower' is hand-painted in delicate pastel tones which gives the cottage an ethereal beauty.

"The Bower"
by
Coalport
Fine Bone China
Made in England

THE BOWER

TECHNICAL DATA

Designer:	Andrew Bill
Modeller:	Andrew Bill
Height:	4", 10.1 cm
Colour:	White; pale turquoise roof; gold window and door frames; green moss
Issued:	1987-1990
Series:	Pastille Burners

PRICING DATA

U.S.	$200.00
Can.	$275.00
U.K.	£150.00

Top: Front view

BRIDGE HOUSE

BRIDGE HOUSE

TECHNICAL DATA

Designer:	Arnold Woolam
Modeller:	Arnold Woolam
Height:	4 ½", 11.9 cm
Colour:	Very light brown walls; light brown and yellow roof; pink, blue and yellow flowers; green moss
Issued:	1976-1981

PRICING DATA

U.S.	$250.00
Can.	$350.00
U.K.	£175.00

Top: Front view
Bottom: Side view

BRINDLEY MEMORIAL WELL, WORMHILL

This well model was commissioned by Sinclairs in a limited edition of 500 pieces.

Backstamp not
available
at press time

BRINDLEY MEMORIAL WELL, WORMHILL

TECHNICAL DATA

Designer:	Arnold Woolam
Modeller:	Arnold Woolam
Height:	5", 12.7 cm
Colour:	White walls; green tower; multicoloured panel
Issued:	1976 in a limited edition of 500
Series:	Derbyshire Well Dressings

PRICING DATA

U.S.	$250.00
Can.	$350.00
U.K.	£175.00

Top: Front view

BRONTE PARSONAGE

This cottage was commissioned by Peter Jones in a limited edition of 500. Emily's faithful dog and her two geese sit at the front of the house.

Backstamp not
available
at press time

BRONTE PARSONAGE

TECHNICAL DATA

Designer:	Tony Sims
Modeller:	Tony Sims
Height:	4", 10.1 cm
Colour:	Grey roof; beige Yorkshire stone
Issued:	1981 in a limited edition of 500
Series:	Historical Buildings of Yorkshire

PRICING DATA

U.S.	$350.00
Can.	$500.00
U.K.	£250.00

Top: Front/side view

CAMELLIA HOUSE

CAMELLIA HOUSE

TECHNICAL DATA

Designer:	Charlotte Royal
Modeller:	Jenny Oliver
Height:	5 ½", 14.0 cm
Colour:	White, decorated with gold spirals and red roses; gold roof, door and flower containers; green base
Issued:	1999 to the present

PRICING DATA

U.S.	$ —
Can.	$ —
U.K.	£115.00

Top: Front view

CAROUSEL

CAROUSEL

TECHNICAL DATA

Designer:	Andrew Bill
Modeller:	Andrew Bill
Height:	4 ¾", 12.1 cm
Colour:	White; pale blue and white chimney; pink door; gold door and window frames; yellow and blue decoration
Issued:	1992 in a limited edition of 500
Series:	Pastille Burners

PRICING DATA

U.S.	$175.00
Can.	$250.00
U.K.	£125.00

Top: Front view

CASCADE COTTAGE, CHATSWORTH

This limited edition cottage was commissioned by Sinclairs.

Backstamp not
available
at press time

CASCADE COTTAGE, CHATSWORTH

TECHNICAL DATA

Designer:	Arnold Woolam
Modeller:	Arnold Woolam
Height:	4", 10.1 cm
Colour:	White; yellow dome; gold outlines; green and yellow decorations
Issued:	c.1978

PRICING DATA

U.S.	$300.00
Can.	$425.00
U.K.	£200.00

Top: Front view

CASTLE

First Variation: Time — 9 o'clock

This castle was reblocked from a 19th-century mould. The time on the clock reads 9 o'clock

> Backstamp not
> available
> at press time

CASTLE
First Variation: Time — 9 o'clock

TECHNICAL DATA

Designer:	Arnold Woolam
Modeller:	Arnold Woolam
Height:	4 ½", 11.9 cm
Colour:	Chestnut brown; white base; green moss
Issued:	1964-1968
Variation:	The Castle (3 o'clock)
Series:	Pastille Burners

PRICING DATA

U.S.	$325.00
Can.	$475.00
U.K.	£225.00

Top: Front view

CASTLE

Second Variation: Time — 3 o'clock

This castle was reblocked from a 19th-century mould. The time on the clock reads 3 o'clock

"Castle"
by
Coalport
ne Bone China
Made in England

CASTLE
Second Variation: Time — 3 o'clock

TECHNICAL DATA

Designer:	Arnold Woolam
Modeller:	Arnold Woolam
Height:	4 ½", 11.9 cm
Colour:	White; brown door and window frames; brown clock; pink, blue and yellow flowers; green moss
Issued:	1976-1981
Variation:	The Castle (9 o'clock)
Series:	Pastille Burners

PRICING DATA

U.S.	$150.00
Can.	$200.00
U.K.	£100.00

Top: Front view
Bottom: Back view

CHANTRY CHAPEL OF ST. MARY'S ON THE BRIDGE, WAKEFIELD

This chapel was commissioned by Peter Jones in a limited edition of 500.

Backstamp not
available
at press time

CHANTRY CHAPEL OF ST. MARY'S ON THE BRIDGE, WAKEFIELD

TECHNICAL DATA

Designer:	Arnold Woolam
Modeller:	Arnold Woolam
Height:	4 ¾", 12.1 cm
Colour:	White; brown window frames; green moss
Issued:	1980 in a limited edition of 500

PRICING DATA

U.S.	$250.00
Can.	$350.00
U.K.	£175.00

Top: Front view
Centre: Back view
Bottom: Side view

CHERRY TREE COTTAGE

First Version: Three Cherry Bushes

Flanked by three fantasy cherry bushes, this cottage is a variation of 'Cherry Villa' which was based on an antique pastille burner.

Backstamp not
available
at press time

CHERRY TREE COTTAGE
First Version: Three Cherry Bushes

TECHNICAL DATA

Designer:	Andrew Bill
Modeller:	Andrew Bill
Height:	4", 10.1 cm
Colour:	White; lilac roof; green steps; mauve bushes; gold outlines
Issued:	1992 in a limited edition of 500
Variation:	Cherry Villa
Series:	Pastille Burners

PRICING DATA

U.S.	$225.00
Can.	$300.00
U.K.	£150.00

Top: Front view

CHERRY VILLA

Second Version: Six Cherry Bushes

Flanked by six fantasy cherry bushes, this charming cottage is based on an antique pastille burner.

CHERRY VILLA
Second Version: Six Cherry Bushes

TECHNICAL DATA

Designer:	Andrew Bill
Modeller:	Andrew Bill
Height:	4 ½", 11.9 cm
Colour:	White; brown-yellow roof; orange chimneys and door; gold door and window frames; six purple cherry bushes; green moss
Issued:	1988-1990
Variation:	Cherry Tree Cottage
Series:	Pastille Burners

PRICING DATA

U.S.	$250.00
Can.	$350.00
U.K.	£175.00

Top: Front view
Bottom: Back view

CHIMNEY HOUSE

The six chimneys which give this house its name would originally have served as real chimneys, channelling the perfume from the burning pastille into a 19th-century room.

"Chimney House"
by
Coalport
Fine Bone China
Made in England

CHIMNEY HOUSE

TECHNICAL DATA

Designer:	Andrew Bill
Modeller:	Andrew Bill
Height:	4", 10.1 cm
Colour:	White; brown bricks and chimney; yellow roof; gold window and door frames
Issued:	1987-1990
Series:	Pastille Burners

PRICING DATA

U.S.	$175.00
Can.	$250.00
U.K.	£125.00

Top: Front view
Centre: Back view

THE CHRISTMAS CHURCH

The Christmas Church
by
Coalport
Fine Bone China
Made in England

THE CHRISTMAS CHURCH

TECHNICAL DATA

Designer:	Tony Sims
Modeller:	Tony Sims
Height:	4", 10.1 cm
Colour:	Light brown walls; white roof; green Christmas tree; multicoloured stained glass windows; brown clock dial
Issued:	1984-1989

PRICING DATA

U.S.	$225.00
Can.	$300.00
U.K.	£150.00

Top: Front view
Centre: Back view
Bottom: Side view

CHRISTMAS COTTAGE

Christmas Cottage
by
Coalport
Fine Bone China
Made in England

CHRISTMAS COTTAGE

TECHNICAL DATA

Designer:	Arnold Woolam
Modeller:	Arnold Woolam
Height:	3 ¼", 8.3 cm
Colour:	White walls with black beams; snow on roof; dark red chimney; dark green tree; white snowman
Issued:	1979-1990

PRICING DATA

U.S.	$150.00
Can.	$225.00
U.K.	£100.00

Top: Front view
Centre: Back view
Bottom: Side view

CLEMATIS COTTAGE

> Backstamp not
> available
> at press time

CLEMATIS COTTAGE

TECHNICAL DATA

Designer:	Andrew Bill
Modeller:	Andrew Bill
Height:	4 ¼", 10.8 cm
Colour:	White; pink roof; gold window and door frames
Issued:	1992 in a limited edition of 500
Series:	Pastille Burners

PRICING DATA

U.S.	$250.00
Can.	$350.00
U.K.	£175.00

Top: Front view

CLERGY HOUSE, ALFRISTON

The National Trust, which owns the Clergy House at Alfriston, East Sussex, commissioned this cottage.

Backstamp not
available
at press time

CLERGY HOUSE, ALFRISTON

TECHNICAL DATA

Designer:	Andrew Bill
Modeller:	Andrew Bill
Height:	2", 5.0 cm
Colour:	White and pale brown brick cottage; black and white half timber; pale greenish-grey roof
Issued:	1986-1990

PRICING DATA

U.S.	$225.00
Can.	$300.00
U.K.	£150.00

Top: Front view
Bottom: Back view

THE CLOCK TOWER

THE CLOCK TOWER

TECHNICAL DATA

Designer:	Arnold Woolam
Modeller:	Arnold Woolam
Height:	4 ½", 11.9 cm
Colour:	White; dark brown door and window frames; light green trim on tower; red clock with dark brown hands and numbers; pink, blue and yellow flowers
Issued:	1980-1984

PRICING DATA

U.S.	$175.00
Can.	$250.00
U.K.	£125.00

Top: Front view

THE COACHING INN

"The Coaching Inn"
by
Coalport
Fine Bone China
Made in England

THE COACHING INN

TECHNICAL DATA

Designer:	Arnold Woolam
Modeller:	Arnold Woolam
Height:	4", 10.1 cm
Colour:	White; black beams; yellow and light brown roof; darker brown window frames; pink, blue and yellow flowers; green moss
Issued:	1977-1990

PRICING DATA

U.S.	$150.00
Can.	$225.00
U.K.	£100.00

Top: Front view
Centre: Back view
Bottom: Side view

COLLECTORS' CLUB SPECIAL

> Backstamp not
> available
> at press time

COLLECTORS' CLUB SPECIAL

TECHNICAL DATA

Designer:	John Woodward
Modeller:	John Woodward
Height:	5 ¼", 13.3 cm
Colour:	White; turquoise roof; gold outlines
Issued:	1985
Variations:	Also known with turquoise and gilt roof

PRICING DATA

U.S.	$225.00
Can.	$300.00
U.K.	£150.00

Top: Front view
Centre: Right side view
Bottom: Left side view

THE COUNTRY COTTAGE

THE COUNTRY COTTAGE

TECHNICAL DATA

Designer:	Arnold Woolam
Modeller:	Arnold Woolam
Height:	4", 10.1 cm
Colour:	White; lilac roof; blue, yellow, green and purple decoration
Issued:	1974-1990
Variation:	Rose Haven
Series:	Pastille Burners

PRICING DATA

U.S.	$150.00
Can.	$225.00
U.K.	£100.00

Top: Front view
Bottom: Back view

COUNTRY RAILWAY STATION

COUNTRY RAILWAY STATION

TECHNICAL DATA

Designer:	Tony Sims
Modeller:	Tony Sims
Height:	3 ½", 8.9 cm
Colour:	White: pale green roof; brown door and window frames; pink, yellow and blue flowers; green moss
Issued:	1982-1989

PRICING DATA

U.S.	$200.00
Can.	$275.00
U.K.	£140.00

Top: Front view
Bottom: Back view

THE CRANE

Delicate awnings soften the angular lines and enhance the attraction of 'The Crane' Inn.

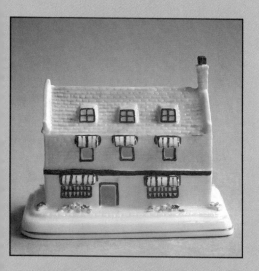

THE CRANE

TECHNICAL DATA

Designer:	Andrew Bill
Modeller:	Andrew Bill
Height:	2 ¾", 7.0 cm
Colour:	Pale brown walls; grey roof; white and green awnings; brown window and door frames
Issued:	1987-1989
Series:	English Inns

PRICING DATA

U.S.	$300.00
Can.	$425.00
U.K.	£200.00

Top: Front view
Bottom: Back view

THE CROOKED COTTAGE

"The Crooked Cottage"
by
Coalport
Fine Bone China
Made in England

THE CROOKED COTTAGE

TECHNICAL DATA

Designer:	Arnold Woolam
Modeller:	Arnold Woolam
Height:	4", 10.1 cm
Colour:	Cream; pale blue roof; brown door, window frames, bench and wheel; green moss
Issued:	1979-1984

PRICING DATA

U.S.	$175.00
Can.	$250.00
U.K.	£125.00

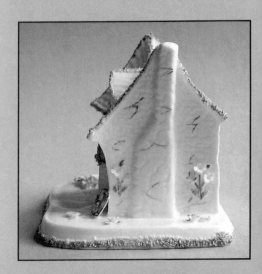

Top: Front view
Centre: Left side view
Bottom: Right side view

THE CROWN

Grand and imposing, like its name. 'The Crown' is typical of so many town inns which can still be seen today in Britain.

THE CROWN

TECHNICAL DATA

Designer:	Andrew Bill
Modeller:	Andrew Bill
Height:	3 ¼", 8.3 cm
Colour:	Brown walls and roof with darker brown timber frames; white windows
Issued:	1987-1989
Series:	English Inns

PRICING DATA

U.S.	$250.00
Can.	$350.00
U.K.	£175.00

Top: Front view
Bottom: Back view

"CRUCK FRAME BARN" HEREFORDSHIRE

"CRUCK FRAME BARN" HEREFORDSHIRE

TECHNICAL DATA

Designer:	Andrew Bill
Modeller:	Andrew Bill
Height:	2 ¾", 7.0 cm
Colour:	Yellow walls; brown-yellow roof; grey doors and frames; green moss
Issued:	1987-1988
Series:	English Barns

PRICING DATA

U.S.	$125.00
Can.	$175.00
U.K.	£90.00

Top: Front view

DOVE COTE

"Dove Cote"
by
Coalport
Fine Bone China
Made in England

DOVE COTE

TECHNICAL DATA

Designer:	Arnold Woolam
Modeller:	Arnold Woolam
Height:	5", 12.7 cm
Colour:	White; yellowish-brown roof with black projections; brown door; white dove; blue and pink flowers; green moss
Issued:	1972-1981
Series:	Pastille Burners

PRICING DATA

U.S.	$165.00
Can.	$225.00
U.K.	£110.00

Top: Front view
Centre: Back view
Bottom: Side view

THE DOWER HOUSE

The Dower House
by
Coalport
Fine Bone China
Made in England

THE DOWER HOUSE

TECHNICAL DATA

Designer:	Arnold Woolam
Modeller:	Arnold Woolam
Height:	4", 10.1 cm
Colour:	White; black window frames; brown door frame; red door; violet, blue and yellow flowers; gold decoration; green moss
Issued:	1980-1983

PRICING DATA

U.S.	$150.00
Can.	$200.00
U.K.	£95.00

Top: Front view

DREAM VILLA

DREAM VILLA

TECHNICAL DATA

Designer:	Andrew Bill
Modeller:	Andrew Bill
Height:	4", 10.1 cm
Colour:	White; pale pink roof; mauve chimneys and doorway; gold window frames and decoration
Issued:	1992 in a limited edition of 500
Variation:	Pantiles
Series:	Pastille Burner

PRICING DATA

U.S.	$250.00
Can.	$350.00
U.K.	£175.00

Top: Front view
Bottom: Back view

THE DUKE OF YORK

A pitched thatched roof adds extra charm to a rambling traditional village inn.

THE DUKE OF YORK

TECHNICAL DATA

Designer:	Andrew Bill
Modeller:	Andrew Bill
Height:	2 ½", 6.4 cm
Colour:	White; yellowish-brown thatched roof; brown door and window frames
Issued:	1987-1989
Series:	English Inns

PRICING DATA

U.S.	$200.00
Can.	$275.00
U.K.	£150.00

Top: Front view
Centre: Back view
Bottom: Front/right side view

ELIZABETHAN COTTAGE

A charming thatched Tudor cottage conjures up memories of a golden English age.

"Elizabethan Cottage"
by
Coalport
Made in England

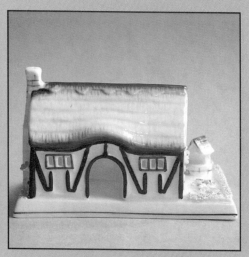

ELIZABETHAN COTTAGE

TECHNICAL DATA

Designer:	Arnold Woolam
Modeller:	Arnold Woolam
Height:	3", 7.6 cm
Colour:	White; brown beams; yellow-brown roof and wishing well; white wheelbarrow of flowers
Issued:	1976-1990

PRICING DATA

U.S.	$150.00
Can.	$200.00
U.K.	£100.00

Top:	Front view
Centre:	Back view
Bottom:	Side view

ENCHANTED CASTLE

ENCHANTED CASTLE

TECHNICAL DATA

Designer:	Charlotte Royal
Modeller:	Jenny Oliver
Height:	4", 10.1 cm
Colour:	White; red-brown roof; beige door; green grass
Issued:	2000 to the present
Series:	Sleeping Beauty

PRICING DATA

U.S.	$ —
Can.	$ —
U.K.	£39.00

Top: Front view
Centre: Back view
Bottom: Removable lid

Note: For other items in this series, see pages 220-221.

ENCHANTED FOLLY

Backstamp not
available
at press time

ENCHANTED FOLLY

TECHNICAL DATA

Designer:	Andrew Bill
Modeller:	Andrew Bill
Height:	4 ¾", 12.1 cm
Colour:	White; pale blue and pink roofs and doors; gold windows, door frames and designs
Issued:	1993 in a limited edition of 500
Variation:	Three Steeples
Series:	Pastille Burners

PRICING DATA

U.S.	$250.00
Can.	$350.00
U.K.	£175.00

Top: Front view

THE FARMHOUSE

The Farmhouse
by
Coalport
Fine Bone China
Made in England

THE FARMHOUSE

TECHNICAL DATA

Designer:	Tony Sims
Modeller:	Tony Sims
Height:	2 ½", 6.4 cm
Colour:	White; yellow and white roof; brown door and window frames; pink and yellow flowers; green moss
Issued:	1980-1984

PRICING DATA

U.S.	$175.00
Can.	$250.00
U.K.	£125.00

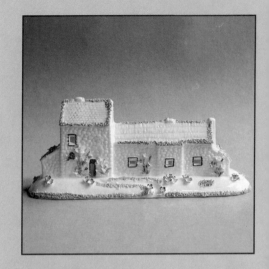

Top: Front view
Centre: Back view
Bottom: Side view

THE FISHERMAN'S COTTAGE

The Fisherman's Cottage
by
Coalport
Fine Bone China
Made in England

THE FISHERMAN'S COTTAGE

TECHNICAL DATA

Designer:	Tony Sims
Modeller:	Tony Sims
Height:	4", 10.1 cm
Colour:	Light brown cottage and chimney; green door; pale green roof; white windows with brown frames; brown boat
Issued:	1983-1989

PRICING DATA

U.S.	$250.00
Can.	$375.00
U.K.	£165.00

Top: Front view
Centre: Left side view
Bottom: Right side view

FORTUNE TOWERS

Backstamp not available at press time

FORTUNE TOWERS

TECHNICAL DATA

Designer:	Andrew Bill
Modeller:	Andrew Bill
Height:	4 ¼", 10.5 cm
Colour:	White; pale blue roof; gold window and door frames
Issued:	1990-1994
Variation:	Barley Sugar House
Series:	Pastille Burners

PRICING DATA

U.S.	$225.00
Can.	$325.00
U.K.	£150.00

Top: Front view

THE GATE HOUSE

THE GATE HOUSE

TECHNICAL DATA

Designer:	Arnold Woolam
Modeller:	Arnold Woolam
Height:	4 ¾", 12.1 cm
Colour:	White; green moss; brown trimmings
Issued:	1965-1981

PRICING DATA

U.S.	$125.00
Can.	$175.00
U.K.	£90.00

Top: Front view

THE GAZEBO

THE GAZEBO

TECHNICAL DATA

Designer:	Andrew Bill
Modeller:	Andrew Bill
Height:	4 ½", 11.9 cm
Colour:	White; brownish-yellow roof; dark blue roof over window and gazebo overhang; gold window and door frames; pale green base
Issued:	1988-1990
Variation:	Summer House, Style Two
Series:	Pastille Burners

PRICING DATA

U.S.	$250.00
Can.	$350.00
U.K.	£175.00

Top: Front view
Centre: Left side view
Bottom: Right side view

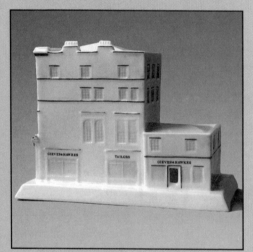

GIEVES & HAWKES NO. 1 SAVILE ROW, LONDON

This model was commissioned by Gieves & Hawkes to commemorate their 200th Anniversary. It was presented to their best customers. Only a few are known to exist.

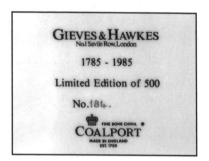

GIEVES & HAWKES
NO. 1 SAVILE ROW, LONDON

TECHNICAL DATA

Designer:	Andrew Bill
Modeller:	Andrew Bill
Height:	4 ½", 11.9 cm
Colour:	White; brown outlines
Issued:	1985

PRICING DATA

U.S.	$ —
Can.	$ Rare
U.K.	£ —

Top: Front view
Bottom: Side view

THE GINGERBREAD HOUSE

THE GINGERBREAD HOUSE

TECHNICAL DATA

Designer:	Tony Sims
Modeller:	Tony Sims
Height:	4", 10.1 cm
Colour:	White; yellow and brown roof; white chimney; dark red door frame and gingerbread men; brown door and steps; pink and yellow flowers; green moss
Issued:	1981-1984

PRICING DATA

U.S.	$250.00
Can.	$350.00
U.K.	£165.00

Top: Front view
Bottom: Side view

HALF MOON HOUSE

HALF MOON HOUSE

TECHNICAL DATA

Designer:	Unknown
Modeller:	Unknown
Height:	3 ¼", 8.3 cm
Colour:	Cream walls; pink on top of towers; gold window and door frames; green trim
Issued:	1992 in a limited edition of 500
Series:	Pastille Burners

PRICING DATA

U.S.	$175.00
Can.	$250.00
U.K.	£125.00

Top: Front view
Bottom: Back view

HUNTING LODGE

Based on an antique pastille burner, the 'Hunting Lodge' with its rounded profile is evocative and unusual.

HUNTING LODGE

TECHNICAL DATA

Designer:	Andrew Bill
Modeller:	Andrew Bill
Height:	3 ½", 8.9 cm
Colour:	White; yellowish-brown roof; brown door; gold door and window frames; green moss
Issued:	1987-1990
Series:	Pastille Burners

PRICING DATA

U.S.	$250.00
Can.	$350.00
U.K.	£175.00

Top: Front view

THE KEEP

THE KEEP

TECHNICAL DATA

Designer:	Tony Sims
Modeller:	Tony Sims
Height:	2", 5.0 cm
Colour:	Cream; brown door and windows; pink and blue flowers; green moss
Issued:	c.1980
Series:	Miniature Cottages

PRICING DATA

U.S.	$100.00
Can.	$140.00
U.K.	£65.00

Top: Front view
Bottom: Back view

KEEPERS COTTAGE

"Keepers Cottage"
by
Coalport
Fine Bone China
Made in England

KEEPERS COTTAGE

TECHNICAL DATA

Designer: Arnold Woolam
Modeller: Arnold Woolam
Height: 3 ½", 8.9 cm
Colour: White; brown chimneys,
             door and gate posts;
             green decoration
Issued: 1964-1990

PRICING DATA

U.S. $165.00
Can. $225.00
U.K.   £115.00

Top: Front view
Centre: Back view
Bottom: Side view

THE KING'S HEAD

Ivy clings to the walls of this welcoming hostelry and, inside, surely there must be bedrooms with low ceilings, creaking floors and four-poster beds.

THE KING'S HEAD

TECHNICAL DATA

Designer:	Andrew Bill
Modeller:	Andrew Bill
Height:	2 ½", 6.4 cm
Colour:	Grey roof; grey vinery; brown door and window frames
Issued:	1987-1989
Series:	English Inns

PRICING DATA

U.S.	$225.00
Can.	$325.00
U.K.	£150.00

Top: Front view
Bottom: Back view

THE LIGHTHOUSE

'The Lighthouse' can be differentiated from the 'Bermuda Lighthouse' by the green band around the tower.

THE LIGHTHOUSE

TECHNICAL DATA

Designer:	Tony Sims
Height:	6 ¼", 15.9 cm
Colour:	Brown cottage; pale green roof; red chimney; white lighthouse with green band; green decoration
Issued:	Unknown
Variations:	Bermuda Lighthouse

PRICING DATA

U.S.	$250.00
Can.	$350.00
U.K.	£175.00

Top: Front view
Bottom: Back view

COTTAGES

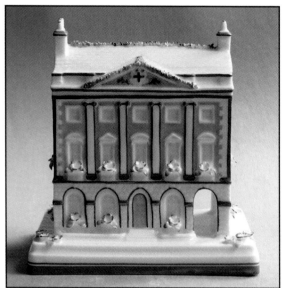

The Mansion House, York

The Old Palace Gatehouse, Richmond, Surrey

The Crown

Mulberry Hall

COTTAGES

Springtime

The Parasol House

The Summer House, Style One

Tiffany Cottage

COTTAGES

The Vinery

Park Folly

Dream Villa

Pantiles

COTTAGES

Summer House, Style Two

The Gazebo

Three Steeples

Enchanted Folly

COTTAGES

Thatched Cottage, First Version

Thatched Cottage, Second Version, Removable Lid

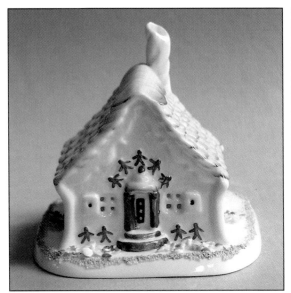

The Gingerbread House

Watchdog Corner

COTTAGES

Camellia House

Orange Blossom Cottage

Orchid Retreat

The Millennium Cottage

DERBYSHIRE WELL DRESSINGS

Old Town Hall Well, Bakewell

Brindley Memorial Well, Wormhill

Ashford in the Water Well

Tissington Hall Well

CHURCHES

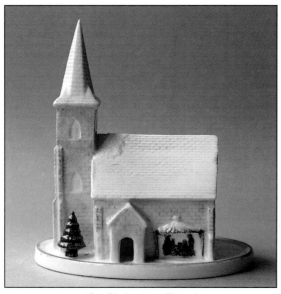

The Christmas Church

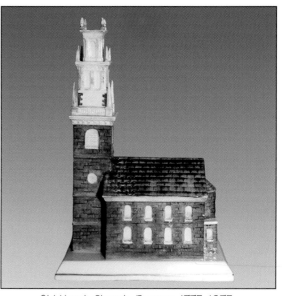

Old North Church, Boston, 1773-1973

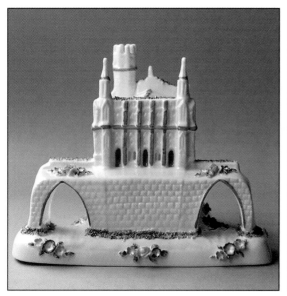

Chantry Chapel of St. Mary's
on the Bridge, Wakefield

Village Church

THE LITTLE CHURCH

<table>
<tr><td>Backstamp not
available
at press time</td></tr>
</table>

THE LITTLE CHURCH

TECHNICAL DATA

Designer:	Tony Sims
Modeller:	Tony Sims
Height:	2", 5.0 cm
Colour:	Cream; pale blue roof; green decoration
Issued:	c.1980
Series:	Miniature Cottages

PRICING DATA

U.S.	$100.00
Can.	$145.00
U.K.	£65.00

Top: Front view

LITTLE GREY RABBITS HOUSE

LITTLE GREY RABBITS HOUSE

TECHNICAL DATA

Designer:	Tony Sims
Modeller:	Tony Sims
Height:	4", 10.1 cm
Colour:	White; reddish-brown roof; green window shutters, door and window frames; black chimney; green trim
Issued:	1981-1983

PRICING DATA

U.S.	$200.00
Can.	$275.00
U.K.	£140.00

Top: Front view
Centre: Back view
Bottom: Side view

Note: For other items in the Little Grey Rabbit series, see pages 196-199.

THE MANSION HOUSE, YORK

'The Mansion House, York' was commissioned by Mulberry Hall.

THE MANSION HOUSE, YORK

TECHNICAL DATA

Designer:	Tony Sims
Modeller:	Tony Sims
Height:	4 ½", 11.9 cm
Colour:	Pink walls; dark brown door frames and trim; yellow roof; white chimney; green moss
Issued:	1982-1986

PRICING DATA

U.S.	$250.00
Can.	$350.00
U.K.	£175.00

Top: Front view
Bottom: Side view

THE MASTER'S HOUSE

THE MASTER'S HOUSE

TECHNICAL DATA

Designer:	Arnold Woolam
Modeller:	Arnold Woolam
Height:	3 ¾", 9.5 cm
Colour:	White; yellow and brown roof; brown beams, window frames and fence; yellow and green trees; grey dog
Issued:	1965-1990

PRICING DATA

U.S.	$150.00
Can.	$225.00
U.K.	£100.00

Top: Front view
Centre: Back view
Bottom: Side view

"MEDIEVAL WOODEN BARN" ESSEX

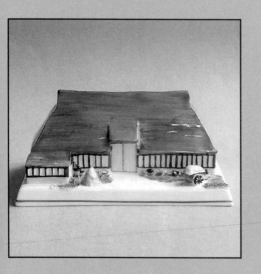

"MEDIEVAL WOODEN BARN" ESSEX

TECHNICAL DATA

Designer:	Andrew Bill
Modeller:	Andrew Bill
Height:	2 ¾", 7.0 cm
Colour:	Brown roof; white wall with brown beams
Issued:	1987-1988
Series:	English Barns

PRICING DATA

U.S.	$135.00
Can.	$200.00
U.K.	£90.00

Top: Front view

THE MILLENNIUM COTTAGE

This cottage, issued in a limited edition of 250, was commissioned by Sinclairs to celebrate the Millennium.

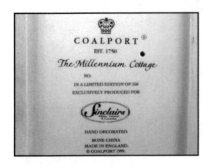

THE MILLENNIUM COTTAGE

TECHNICAL DATA

Designer:	Unknown
Modeller:	Jenny Oliver
Height:	6 ½", 16.5 cm
Colour:	White, decorated with pink roses and green leaves; deep blue windows with gold lattice; beige dome; green turrets and floor decorated with gold stars
Issued:	1999 in a limited edition of 250

PRICING DATA

U.S.	$ —
Can.	$ —
U.K.	£250.00

Top: Front view
Bottom: Side view

MOTHER HUBBARDS COTTAGE

Mother Hubbards Cottage
by
Coalport
Made in England

MOTHER HUBBARDS COTTAGE

TECHNICAL DATA

Designer:	Tony Sims
Modeller:	Tony Sims
Height:	2 ¾", 7.0 cm
Colour:	White; yellow and brown roof trimmed with green; white chimneys; brown doors and window frames; pink and yellow flowers
Issued:	1982-1984

PRICING DATA

U.S.	$200.00
Can.	$275.00
U.K.	£140.00

Top: Front view
Bottom: Back view

MOUSEY THOMSOMS COTTAGE

This cottage, commissioned by Peter Jones, Yorkshire, was issued in a limited edition of 500.

Backstamp not
available
at press time

MOUSEY THOMSOMS COTTAGE

TECHNICAL DATA

Designer:	Tony Sims
Modeller:	Tony Sims
Height:	2 ½", 6.4 cm
Colour:	White building; brown timbers; grey roof
Issued:	1985 in a limited edition of 500
Series:	Historical Buildings of Yorkshire

PRICING DATA

U.S.	$250.00
Can.	$350.00
U.K.	£175.00

Top: Front/side view

MULBERRY HALL

This model was commissioned by Mulberry Hall in 1990 and is still available.

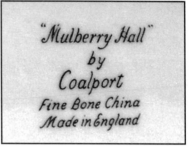

"*Mulberry Hall*"
by
Coalport
Fine Bone China
Made in England

MULBERRY HALL

TECHNICAL DATA

Designer:	Tony Sims
Modeller:	Tony Sims
Height:	5 ¾", 14.6 cm
Colour:	White; yellow roof; gold beams, windows and door frames
Issued:	1990 to the present

PRICING DATA

U.S.	$ —
Can.	$ —
U.K.	£175.00

Top: Front view
Bottom: Side view

Note: An earlier version of Mulberry Hall modelled by Arnold Woolham was produced from 1983 to c.1990, the main differences being the roof, chimney and colour.

THE NATIVITY SCENE

THE NATIVITY SCENE

TECHNICAL DATA

Designer:	Arnold Woolam
Modeller:	Arnold Woolam
Height:	3", 7.6 cm
Colour:	Light beige walls; dark brown tree; light brown and yellow roof; Mary dressed in blue; blue blanket on manger
Issued:	1976-1977

PRICING DATA

U.S.	$175.00
Can.	$250.00
U.K.	£125.00

Top:	Front view
Centre:	Back view
Bottom:	Side view

THE NIGHTINGALE

THE NIGHTINGALE

TECHNICAL DATA

Designer:	Andrew Bill
Modeller:	Andrew Bill
Height:	2 ¾", 7.0 cm
Colour:	Peach walls; grey roof; brown door and window frames
Issued:	1987-1989
Series:	English Inns

PRICING DATA

U.S.	$225.00
Can.	$325.00
U.K.	£150.00

Top: Front view
Bottom: Back view

THE OAST HOUSE

THE OAST HOUSE

TECHNICAL DATA

Designer:	Arnold Woolam
Modeller:	Arnold Woolam
Height:	4 ½", 11.9 cm
Colour:	Pale brown barn; white tower; pale green roofs; green moss
Issued:	1981-1984

PRICING DATA

U.S.	$225.00
Can.	$325.00
U.K.	£145.00

Top: Front view
Centre: Back view
Bottom: Side view

THE OLD CURIOSITY SHOP

"The Old Curiosity Shop"
by
Coalport
Fine Bone China
Made in England

THE OLD CURIOSITY SHOP

TECHNICAL DATA

Designer:	Unknown
Modeller:	Arnold Woolam
Height:	4 ¾", 12.1 cm
Colour:	White; brown timber beams; light brown door and window frames; green and black lamp post; green moss
Issued:	1977-1990

PRICING DATA

U.S.	$150.00
Can.	$200.00
U.K.	£100.00

Top: Front view
Centre: Back view
Bottom: Side view

OLD NORTH CHURCH, BOSTON 1773-1973

To celebrate the 200th Anniversary of the Old North Church, Shreve, Crump and Lowe Ltd. commissioned this piece in a limited edition of 50 pieces.

Backstamp not
available
at press time

OLD NORTH CHURCH, BOSTON 1773-1973

TECHNICAL DATA

Designer:	Arnold Woolam
Modeller:	Arnold Woolam
Height:	Unknown
Colour:	Red brick church; grey roof and door; white tower and windows
Issued:	1973 in a limited edition of 50

PRICING DATA

U.S.	$	—
Can.	$	Rare
U.K.	£	—

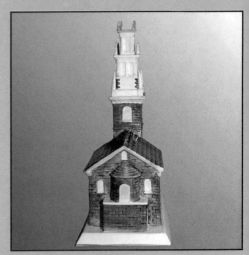

Top: Front view
Centre: Back view
Bottom: Side view

THE OLD PALACE GATEHOUSE RICHMOND SURREY

The Old Palace Gatehouse
Richmond
Surrey
by
Coalport
Fine Bone China
Made in England

THE OLD PALACE GATEHOUSE RICHMOND SURREY

TECHNICAL DATA

Designer: Tony Sims
Modeller: Tony Sims
Height: 4 ½", 11.9 cm
Colour: Red-brown brick building; white roof; red chimneys; yellow door; green grass
Issued: 1984-1989

PRICING DATA

U.S. $175.00
Can. $250.00
U.K. £125.00

Top: Front view
Bottom: Side view

OLD TOWN HALL WELL, BAKEWELL

This model was commissioned by Sinclairs in a limited edition of 500.

OLD TOWN HALL WELL, BAKEWELL

TECHNICAL DATA

Designer:	Arnold Woolam
Modeller:	Arnold Woolam
Height:	3 ¾", 9.5 cm
Colour:	Grey-blue building decorated with a multicoloured panel representing the 'Year of the Child'
Issued:	1983 in a limited edition of 500
Series:	Derbyshire Well Dressings

PRICING DATA

U.S.	$250.00
Can.	$350.00
U.K.	£175.00

Top: Front view

THE OLD WOMANS SHOE

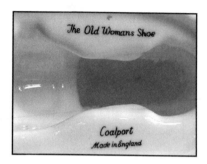

THE OLD WOMANS SHOE

TECHNICAL DATA

Designer:	Tony Sims
Modeller:	Tony Sims
Height:	2 ½", 6.4 cm
Colour:	White boot; blue door and window frames; dark red chimney; brown shoe sole and heel; green grass and trim; pink and yellow flowers
Issued:	1981-1984

PRICING DATA

U.S.	$175.00
Can.	$250.00
U.K.	£125.00

Top: Front view
Bottom: Back view

ORANGE BLOSSOM COTTAGE

ORANGE BLOSSOM COTTAGE

TECHNICAL DATA

Designer:	Charlotte Royal
Modeller:	Jenny Oliver
Height:	5 ¼", 13.3 cm
Colour:	White, orange, green and gold trimmings
Issued:	1999 to the present

PRICING DATA

U.S.	$ —
Can.	$ —
U.K.	£105.00

Top: Front view

THE ORANGERY

Backstamp not
available
at press time

THE ORANGERY

TECHNICAL DATA

Designer:	Unknown
Height:	4 ¼", 10.8 cm
Colour:	Creamy-yellow walls; brown beams; yellow-green roof; pale turquoise decoration
Issued:	1992 in a limited edition of 500
Series:	Pastille Burners

PRICING DATA

U.S.	$175.00
Can.	$250.00
U.K.	£125.00

Top: Front view
Bottom: Back view

ORCHID RETREAT

ORCHID RETREAT

TECHNICAL DATA

Designer:	Charlotte Royal
Modeller:	Jenny Oliver
Height:	5", 12.7 cm
Colour:	White; purple, green and orange decoration; gold roof
Issued:	1999 to the present

PRICING DATA

U.S.	$ —
Can.	$ —
U.K.	£125.00

Top: Front view

PAGODA HOUSE

PAGODA HOUSE

TECHNICAL DATA

Designer:	Arnold Woolam
Modeller:	Arnold Woolam
Height:	4", 10.1 cm
Colour:	White; brown door and window frames; gold trim; pink, blue and yellow flowers
Issued:	1976-1984

PRICING DATA

U.S.	$150.00
Can.	$225.00
U.K.	£100.00

Top: Front view
Bottom: Side view

PANTILES

The red convex roofing tiles lie behind this cottage's name and give it a charming and individual character.

PANTILES

TECHNICAL DATA

Designer:	Andrew Bill
Modeller:	Andrew Bill
Height:	4", 10.1 cm
Colour:	Pearl building; red roof and awnings; blue door; gold window frames
Issued:	1988-1990
Variation:	Dream Villa
Series:	Pastille Burners

PRICING DATA

U.S.	$225.00
Can.	$325.00
U.K.	£150.00

Top: Front view
Bottom: Back view

THE PARASOL HOUSE

'The Parasol House,' with its quaint umbrella-shaped roof, is one of the reblocked Coalport moulds from the 1800s.

THE PARASOL HOUSE

TECHNICAL DATA

Designer:	Unknown
Modeller:	Unknown
Height:	4", 10.1 cm
Colour:	White; brown window and door frames; purple, yellow, orange and blue flowers; light brown moss
Issued:	1964-1990
Variations:	Springtime Cottage
Series:	Pastille Burners

PRICING DATA

U.S.	$150.00
Can.	$225.00
U.K.	£100.00

Top: Front view
Centre: Back view
Bottom: Side view

PARK FOLLY

An antique pastille burner was the inspiration for this remarkable creation with its sumptuous pink roof and imposing statues standing sentinel at the front door.

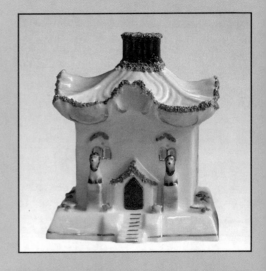

PARK FOLLY

TECHNICAL DATA

Designer:	Andrew Bill
Modeller:	Andrew Bill
Height:	4 ¼", 10.8 cm
Colour:	White; pink roof; gold window and frames; pale blue dogs; pale blue, orange and mauve decoration
Issued:	1987-1990
Variations:	The Vinery
Series:	Pastille Burners

PRICING DATA

U.S.	$225.00
Can.	$325.00
U.K.	£150.00

Top: Front view
Bottom: Back view

PARK LODGE

This cottage was reblocked from a 19th-century mould.

"Park Lodge"
by
Coalport
Fine Bone China
Made in England.

PARK LODGE

TECHNICAL DATA

Designer:	Unknown
Modeller:	Unknown
Height:	4 ¾", 12.1 cm
Colour:	White; brown door and window frames; green moss
Issued:	1964-1982

PRICING DATA

U.S.	$150.00
Can.	$225.00
U.K.	£100.00

Top: Front view
Bottom: Back view

THE PROVISION SHOP

THE PROVISION SHOP

TECHNICAL DATA

Designer:	Tony Sims
Modeller:	Tony Sims
Height:	4 ¼", 10.8 cm
Colour:	White; yellow roof; brown beams and window frames
Issued:	1984-1989

PRICING DATA

U.S.	$200.00
Can.	$275.00
U.K.	£135.00

Top:	Front view
Centre:	Back view
Bottom:	Side view

QUEEN MARY'S DOLLS HOUSE

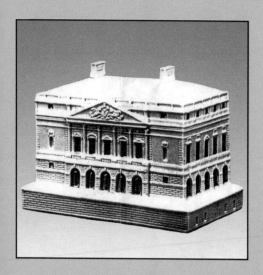

This model, which came with a certificate of authenticity, is extremely rare. Due to the complexity of the model and the difficulty in firing, less than ten houses are thought to exist.

Backstamp not
available
at press time

QUEEN MARY'S DOLLS HOUSE

TECHNICAL DATA

Designer:	Tony Sims
Modeller:	Tony Sims
Height:	Unknown
Colour:	Unknown
Issued:	1984

PRICING DATA

U.S.	Extremely rare
Can.	Less than 10 models
U.K.	are thought to exist

Top: Front view

RED HOUSE

"Red House"
by
Coalport
Fine Bone China
Made in England

RED HOUSE

TECHNICAL DATA

Designer:	Arnold Woolam
Modeller:	Arnold Woolam
Height:	5", 12.7 cm
Colour:	Dark red brick; white trees, birds, windows and doors outlined in gold; light brown roof
Issued:	1968-1984
Series:	Pastille Burners

PRICING DATA

U.S.	$150.00
Can.	$225.00
U.K.	£100.00

Top: Front view
Centre: Back view
Bottom: Side view

ROBERT BURNS' COTTAGE

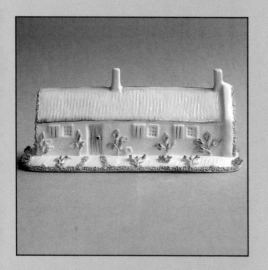

ROBERT BURNS' COTTAGE

TECHNICAL DATA

Designer:	Tony Sims
Modeller:	Tony Sims
Height:	2 ½", 6.4 cm
Colour:	White; yellow and brown roof; green trees; purple flowers; green moss
Issued:	1980-1983

PRICING DATA

U.S.	$165.00
Can.	$225.00
U.K.	£110.00

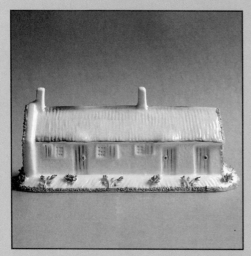

Top: Front view
Centre: Back view
Bottom: Side view

ROSE ARBOUR

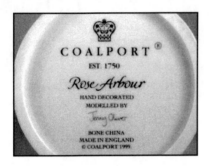

ROSE ARBOUR

TECHNICAL DATA

Designer:	Charlotte Royal
Modeller:	Jenny Oliver
Height:	4 ¼", 10.8 cm
Colour:	White; red roses; green leaves; brown lattice
Issued:	1999 to the present

PRICING DATA

U.S.	$ —
Can.	$ —
U.K.	£95.00

Top: Front view

ROSE HAVEN

ROSE HAVEN

TECHNICAL DATA

Designer:	Arnold Woolam
Modeller:	Arnold Woolam
Height:	4 ¼", 10.8 cm
Colour:	White walls; pale green roof; gold window and door frames; green moss
Issued:	1992 in a limited edition of 500
Variations:	The Country Cottage
Series:	Pastille Burners

PRICING DATA

U.S.	$225.00
Can.	$325.00
U.K.	£150.00

Top: Front view
Bottom: Back view

THE ROUNDHOUSE

THE ROUNDHOUSE

TECHNICAL DATA

Designer:	Tony Sims
Modeller:	Tony Sims
Height:	4 ¼", 10.8 cm
Colour:	Pale brown walls; darker brown door; white window frames; dark red roof; yellow, pink and purple flowers; green moss
Issued:	1982-1984

PRICING DATA

U.S.	$300.00
Can.	$475.00
U.K.	£200.00

Top: Front view

THE ROYAL OAK

What could be more English than this traditional timbered inn with its projecting upper storey?

THE ROYAL OAK

TECHNICAL DATA

Designer:	Andrew Bill
Modeller:	Andrew Bill
Height:	2 ¾", 7.0 cm
Colour:	White with brown timber frames; grey roof; green moss
Issued:	1987-1989
Series:	English Inns

PRICING DATA

U.S.	$225.00
Can.	$325.00
U.K.	£150.00

Top: Front view
Centre: Back view
Bottom: Front/side view

ROYAL PUMP ROOM HARROGATE NORTH YORKSHIRE

Built in 1842 to house one of Harrogate's first medicinal springs. The 'Royal Pump Room' was commissioned by Peter Jones in a limited edition of 500.

Backstamp not
available
at press time

ROYAL PUMP ROOM
HARROGATE
NORTH YORKSHIRE

TECHNICAL DATA

Designer:	Tony Sims
Modeller:	Tony Sims
Height:	4 ¼", 10.8 cm
Colour:	White; green roof; pink, yellow and blue flowers; green decoration
Issued:	1984 in a limited edition of 500

PRICING DATA

U.S.	$250.00
Can.	$350.00
U.K.	£175.00

Top: Front view

RUSTIC COTTAGE

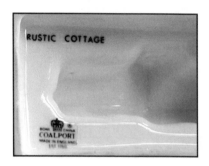

RUSTIC COTTAGE

TECHNICAL DATA

Designer:	Tony Sims
Modeller:	Tony Sims
Height:	2", 5.0 cm
Colour:	White; yellow roof; brown doors; green moss
Issued:	c.1980
Series:	Miniature Cottages

PRICING DATA

U.S.	$100.00
Can.	$150.00
U.K.	£65.00

Top: Front view
Bottom: Back view

SECRET RETREAT

Backstamp not
available
at press time

SECRET RETREAT

TECHNICAL DATA

Designer:	Andrew Bill
Modeller:	Andrew Bill
Height:	3 ¾", 9.5 cm
Colour:	White walls; pale turquoise roof; gold outlines; pale pink, yellow and green decoration
Issued:	1992 in a limited edition of 500
Variation:	The Arbour
Series:	Pastille Burners

PRICING DATA

U.S.	$250.00
Can.	$350.00
U.K.	£175.00

Top: Front view

SHAKESPEARE'S BIRTHPLACE STRATFORD-UPON-AVON

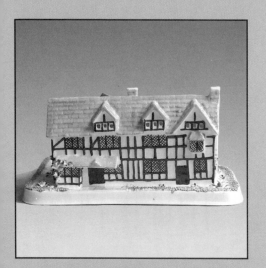

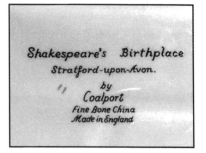

SHAKESPEARE'S BIRTHPLACE STRATFORD-UPON-AVON

TECHNICAL DATA

Designer:	Tony Sims
Modeller:	Tony Sims
Height:	3 ½", 8.9 cm
Colour:	White; brown roof and timber frames; green decoration
Issued:	1981-1984

PRICING DATA

U.S.	$225.00
Can.	$325.00
U.K.	£165.00

Top: Front view
Bottom: Back view

SIX CHIMNEYS LOWER KIRKGATE WAKEFIELD

This mid 16th-century Elizabethan building was constructed in 1556 and tragically demolished in the early 1940s. Commissioned by Peter Jones of Wakefield, this cottage was issued in a limited edition of 500.

Backstamp not
available
at press time

SIX CHIMNEYS, LOWER KIRKGATE WAKEFIELD

TECHNICAL DATA

Designer:	Tony Sims
Modeller:	Tony Sims
Height:	4 ½", 11.9 cm
Colour:	Cream; brown beams and window frames
Issued:	1980 in a limited edition of 500

PRICING DATA

U.S.	$275.00
Can.	$375.00
U.K.	£185.00

Top: Front view
Bottom: Back view

SPRINGTIME COTTAGE

This cottage, as the Parasol House, was reblocked from a 19th-century mould.

SPRINGTIME COTTAGE

TECHNICAL DATA

Designer:	Unknown
Modeller:	Unknown
Height:	4", 10.1 cm
Colour:	White; cream roof with pale turquoise decoration; gold window, door and step frames; pale blue and pale yellow decoration on base
Issued:	1993 in a limited edition of 500
Variation:	The Parasol House
Series:	Pastille Burners

PRICING DATA

U.S.	$250.00
Can.	$350.00
U.K.	£175.00

Top: Front view
Bottom: Back view

THE SUMMER HOUSE

Style One

This cottage was reblocked from a 19th-century mould.

THE SUMMER HOUSE
Style One

TECHNICAL DATA

Designer:	Unknown
Modeller:	Unknown
Height:	4", 10.1 cm
Colour:	White; brown window and door frames; brown moss; multicoloured flowers
Issued:	1964-1983
Variation:	Tiffany Cottage

PRICING DATA

U.S.	$165.00
Can.	$225.00
U.K.	£110.00

Top: Front view
Centre: Back view
Bottom: Side view

SUMMER HOUSE

Style Two

Backstamp not
available
at press time

SUMMER HOUSE
Style Two

TECHNICAL DATA

Designer:	Andrew Bill
Modeller:	Andrew Bill
Height:	4 ½", 11.9 cm
Colour:	White; yellow roof; gold outlines; lilac, green and yellow decoration
Issued:	1992 in a limited edition of 500
Variation:	The Gazebo
Series:	Pastille Burners

PRICING DATA

U.S.	$250.00
Can.	$350.00
U.K.	£175.00

Top: Front view
Bottom: Side view

SUMMER PALACE

Backstamp not
available
at press time

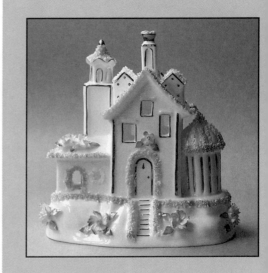

SUMMER PALACE

TECHNICAL DATA

Designer:	Andrew Bill
Modeller:	Andrew Bill
Height:	4 ¾", 12.1 cm
Colour:	White; gold outlines; green and yellow decoration
Issued:	1992 in a limited edition of 500
Variations:	The Bell Tower
Series:	Pastille Burners

PRICING DATA

U.S.	$250.00
Can.	$350.00
U.K.	£175.00

Top: Front view

SUMMER RETREAT

Based on an antique pastille burner, the red-tiled 'Summer Retreat' conjures up images of long-ago holidays in the August countryside.

SUMMER RETREAT

TECHNICAL DATA

Designer:	Andrew Bill
Modeller:	Andrew Bill
Height:	4 ¼", 10.8 cm
Colour:	White; red-brown tiled roof and door; gold window and door frames
Issued:	1987-1990
Series:	Pastille Burners

PRICING DATA

U.S.	$250.00
Can.	$375.00
U.K.	£165.00

Top: Front view
Bottom: Back view

"TILED GRANARY" SURREY

"TILED GRANARY" SURREY

TECHNICAL DATA

Designer:	Andrew Bill
Modeller:	Andrew Bill
Height:	2 ½", 5.7 cm
Colour:	Light brown and grey walls; dark brown roof; green grass, tree and trim
Issued:	1987-1988
Series:	English Barns

PRICING DATA

U.S.	$135.00
Can.	$200.00
U.K.	£90.00

Top: Front view

"TIMBER FRAMED GRANARY" SUSSEX

"TIMBER FRAMED GRANARY" SUSSEX

TECHNICAL DATA

Designer:	Andrew Bill
Modeller:	Andrew Bill
Height:	2 ¾", 7.0 cm
Colour:	White walls with brown beams; dark brown door; light brown roof; green moss
Issued:	1987-1988
Series:	English Barns

PRICING DATA

U.S.	$135.00
Can.	$200.00
U.K.	£90.00

Top: Front view
Bottom: Back view

SWISS COTTAGE

> *"Swiss Cottage"*
> *by*
> *Coalport*
> *Fine Bone China*
> *Made in England*

SWISS COTTAGE

TECHNICAL DATA

Designer:	Arnold Woolam
Modeller:	Arnold Woolam
Height:	3 ½", 8.9 cm
Colour:	White; light brown walls and steps; darker brown window and door frames; dark red chimney; pink, blue and yellow flowers; green and gold trim
Issued:	1976-1982

PRICING DATA

U.S.	$175.00
Can.	$250.00
U.K.	£125.00

Top: Front view
Centre: Back view
Bottom: Side view

TEMPLE HOUSE

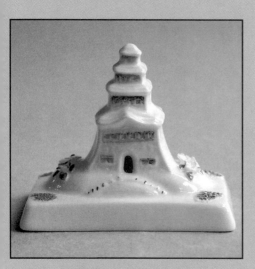

TEMPLE HOUSE

TECHNICAL DATA

Designer:	Tony Sims
Modeller:	Tony Sims
Height:	2 ½", 6.4 cm
Colour:	White; gold window frames; brown door; pink and yellow flowers; green grass
Issued:	c.1980
Series:	Miniature Cottages

PRICING DATA

U.S.	$75.00
Can.	$100.00
U.K.	£50.00

Top: Front view
Centre: Back view
Bottom: Side view

THATCHED COTTAGE

First Version

This cottage is from a reblocked 19th-century mould.

THATCHED COTTAGE
First Version

TECHNICAL DATA

Designer:	Unknown
Modeller:	Unknown
Height:	4", 10.1 cm
Colour:	White; yellow roof; brown chimneys and door; pink and green moss
Issued:	1964-1982
Series:	Pastille Burners

PRICING DATA

U.S.	$175.00
Can.	$250.00
U.K.	£125.00

Top: Front view
Bottom: Back view

THATCHED COTTAGE

Second Version

This cottage has a removable roof.

"Thatched Cottage"
by
Coalport
Fine Bone China
Made in England.

THATCHED COTTAGE
Second Version

TECHNICAL DATA

Designer:	Unknown
Modeller:	Unknown
Height:	4", 10.1 cm
Colour:	White; yellowish-brown removable roof; red-brown chimneys and door; rose-pink and green moss
Issued:	c.1964

PRICING DATA

U.S.	$250.00
Can.	$350.00
U.K.	£175.00

Top: Front view
Centre: Back view
Bottom: Removable roof

32 WINDSOR GARDENS, LONDON (PADDINGTON BEAR'S HOME)

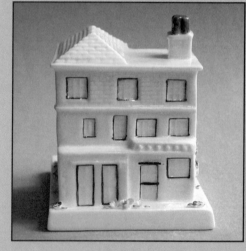

32 WINDSOR GARDENS, LONDON (PADDINGTON BEAR'S HOME)

TECHNICAL DATA

Designer:	Tony Sims
Modeller:	Tony Sims
Height:	4 ¼", 10.8 cm
Colour:	Cream; brown door and window frames; brown chimneys; green tree
Issued:	1983-1984

PRICING DATA

U.S.	$300.00
Can.	$450.00
U.K.	£200.00

Top: Front view
Bottom: Back view

Note: For other items in the Paddington Bear series,
see pages 200-215.

THREE STEEPLES

The three ornate yellow steeples which give this cottage its name are bedecked with flowers and moss.

"Three Steeples"
by
Coalport
Fine Bone China
Made in England

THREE STEEPLES

TECHNICAL DATA

Designer:	Andrew Bill
Modeller:	Andrew Bill
Height:	4 ¾", 12.1 cm
Colour:	White; yellow steeples; red-brown doors; gold frames
Issued:	1988-1990
Variations:	Enchanted Folly
Series:	Pastille Burners

PRICING DATA

U.S.	$250.00
Can.	$350.00
U.K.	£175.00

Top: Front view

TIFFANY COTTAGE

This cottage was commissioned by Tiffany & Co.

TIFFANY COTTAGE

TECHNICAL DATA

Designer:	Unknown
Modeller:	Unknown
Height:	4 ¼", 10.8 cm
Colour:	Blue walls; white roof decorated with blue, orange and purple handmade flowers; white door; brown window and door frames; green moss
Issued:	c.1970
Variation:	The Summer House, Style One
Series:	Pastille Burners

PRICING DATA

U.S.	$300.00
Can.	$450.00
U.K.	£200.00

Top: Front view
Centre: Back view
Bottom: Side view

TISSINGTON HALL WELL

Commissioned by Sinclairs, this well was issued in a limited edition of 500.

> Backstamp not
> available
> at press time

TISSINGTON HALL WELL

TECHNICAL DATA

Designer:	Arnold Woolam
Modeller:	Arnold Woolam
Height:	4 ¼", 10.8 cm
Colour:	White; green roof; multicoloured design "Saint Cecilia"
Issued:	In a limited edition of 500
Series:	Derbyshire Well Dressings

PRICING DATA

U.S.	$300.00
Can.	$450.00
U.K.	£200.00

Top: Front view

THE TOADSTOOL HOUSE

THE TOADSTOOL HOUSE

TECHNICAL DATA

Designer:	Unknown
Modeller:	Unknown
Height:	5 ¾", 14.6 cm
Colour:	Cream stem; yellow and brown cap; pale green door and steps; blue door and window frames; brown chimney
Issued:	1981-1982

PRICING DATA

U.S.	$200.00
Can.	$300.00
U.K.	£140.00

Top: Front view
Bottom: Back view

THE TOLL HOUSE

"The Toll House"
by
Coalport
Fine Bone China
Made in England

THE TOLL HOUSE

TECHNICAL DATA

Designer:	Arnold Woolam
Modeller:	Arnold Woolam
Height:	5", 12.7 cm
Colour:	White; red latticed windows; white roof with green leaves; brown door frame; yellowish-green base with red and yellow flowers; blue trim
Issued:	1974-1981

PRICING DATA

U.S.	$165.00
Can.	$225.00
U.K.	£110.00

Top: Front view
Bottom: Side view

THE TOWERS

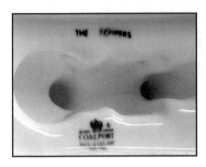

THE TOWERS

TECHNICAL DATA

Designer:	Tony Sims
Modeller:	Tony Sims
Height:	3", 7.6 cm
Colour:	White; pale blue roof; brown door; green moss
Issued:	c.1980
Series:	Miniature Cottages

PRICING DATA

U.S.	$100.00
Can.	$150.00
U.K.	£65.00

Top: Front view
Bottom: Back view

THE TOY SHOP

The Toy Shop
by
Coalport
Fine Bone China
Made in England

THE TOY SHOP

TECHNICAL DATA

Designer:	Tony Sims
Modeller:	Tony Sims
Height:	3 ½", 8.9 cm
Colour:	White; brown roof with snow; brown beams, door and shutters
Issued:	1983-1989
Series:	Pastille Burners

PRICING DATA

U.S.	$200.00
Can.	$275.00
U.K.	£145.00

Top: Front view
Bottom: Side view

TUDOR COTTAGE

TUDOR COTTAGE

TECHNICAL DATA

Designer:	Tony Sims
Modeller:	Tony Sims
Height:	2 ¼", 5.7 cm
Colour:	White; brown beams; green roof
Issued:	c.1980
Series:	Miniature Cottages

PRICING DATA

U.S.	$125.00
Can.	$175.00
U.K.	£75.00

Top: Front view
Bottom: Back view

TWIN TOWERS

Backstamp not
available
at press time

TWIN TOWERS

TECHNICAL DATA

Designer:	Arnold Woolam
Modeller:	Arnold Woolam
Height:	3 ½", 8.9 cm
Colour:	White; red door and chimneys; brown window and door frames; yellowish-brown tree trunks with pink, blue, purple and yellow flowers; green moss
Issued:	1972-1981

PRICING DATA

U.S.	$150.00
Can.	$200.00
U.K.	£100.00

Top: Front view

TWO CHIMNEYS

```
Backstamp not
available
at press time
```

TWO CHIMNEYS

TECHNICAL DATA

Designer:	Tony Sims
Modeller:	Tony Sims
Height:	4 ¼", 10.8 cm
Colour:	Brown and white upper walls; yellow-brown lower walls; grey-blue roof; brown chimney
Issued:	1987

PRICING DATA

U.S.	$175.00
Can.	$250.00
U.K.	£115.00

Top: Front view

TYROLEAN CASTLE

"Tyrolean Castle"
by
Coalport
Fine Bone China
Made in England

TYROLEAN CASTLE

TECHNICAL DATA

Designer:	Arnold Woolam
Modeller:	Arnold Woolam
Height:	4", 10.1 cm
Colour:	Pale brown walls: darker brown window and door frames; pink, blue and yellow flowers; green moss
Issued:	1976-1984

PRICING DATA

U.S.	$150.00
Can.	$225.00
U.K.	£100.00

Top: Front view
Centre: Back view
Bottom: Side view

"TYTHE BARN" WORCESTERSHIRE

"TYTHE BARN" WORCESTERSHIRE

TECHNICAL DATA

Designer:	Andrew Bill
Modeller:	Andrew Bill
Height:	2 ½", 6.4 cm
Colour:	Brown walls; dark grey roof; white windows; green grass, tree and moss
Issued:	1987-1988
Series:	English Barns

PRICING DATA

U.S.	$135.00
Can.	$200.00
U.K.	£90.00

Top: Front view
Bottom: Side view

THE UMBRELLA HOUSE

Based on Coalport's original 19th-century mould, the ornate 'Umbrella House' was reintroduced in 1964 and is ever popular with collectors.

THE UMBRELLA HOUSE

TECHNICAL DATA

Designer:	Unknown
Modeller:	Unknown
Height:	4 ½", 11.9 cm
Colour:	White; brown door and window frames; green decoration
Issued:	1964-1990
Series:	Pastille Burners

PRICING DATA

U.S.	$150.00
Can.	$225.00
U.K.	£100.00

Top: Front view
Bottom: Back view

THE VILLA

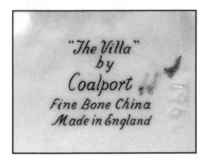

THE VILLA

TECHNICAL DATA

Designer:	Arnold Woolam
Modeller:	Arnold Woolam
Height:	4 ¾", 12.1 cm
Colour:	Cream; gold frames;
	pink latticed windows
Issued:	1968-1981

PRICING DATA

U.S.	$175.00
Can.	$250.00
U.K.	£115.00

Top:	Front view
Centre:	Back view
Bottom:	Side view

VILLAGE CHURCH

The bells ring out, calling the faithful of another age to prayer. This reproduction of a traditional fine bone china church would grace any collection.

"Village Church"
by
Coalport
Fine Bone China
Made in England.

VILLAGE CHURCH

TECHNICAL DATA

Designer:	Arnold Woolam
Modeller:	Arnold Woolam
Height:	5 ¼", 13.3 cm
Colour:	White; brown doors and window frames; green decoration
Issued:	1970-1990

PRICING DATA

U.S.	$185.00
Can.	$275.00
U.K.	£125.00

Top:	Front view
Centre:	Back view
Bottom:	Side view

THE VILLAGE CRICKET PAVILLION

THE VILLAGE CRICKET PAVILLION

TECHNICAL DATA

Designer:	Tony Sims
Modeller:	Tony Sims
Height:	2 ½", 6.4 cm
Colour:	White; green window and door frames; dark brown chimney; clock outlined in dark brown; green moss; pink, blue and yellow flowers
Issued:	1980-1984

PRICING DATA

U.S.	$175.00
Can.	$250.00
U.K.	£125.00

Top: Front view
Centre: Back view
Bottom: Side view

VILLAGE INN

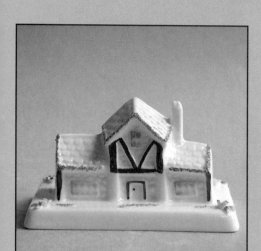

VILLAGE INN

TECHNICAL DATA

Designer:	Tony Sims
Modeller:	Tony Sims
Height:	2", 5.0 cm
Colour:	White; brown beams; pale blue roof; green moss
Issued:	c.1980
Series:	Miniature Cottages

PRICING DATA

U.S.	$90.00
Can.	$135.00
U.K.	£60.00

Top: Front view
Bottom: Back view

THE VILLAGE SCHOOL

THE VILLAGE SCHOOL

TECHNICAL DATA

Designer:	Tony Sims
Modeller:	Tony Sims
Height:	3", 7.6 cm
Colour:	White; brown roof; green door
Issued:	1982-1984

PRICING DATA

U.S.	$200.00
Can.	$300.00
U.K.	£140.00

Top: Front view
Centre: Back view
Bottom: Side view

THE VILLAGE SHOP

THE VILLAGE SHOP

TECHNICAL DATA

Designer:	Tony Sims
Modeller:	Tony Sims
Height:	2 ¼" x 3 ¼", 5.7 x 8.3 cm
Colour:	White; brown trim; yellow roof; green moss
Issued:	c.1980
Series:	Miniature Cottages

PRICING DATA

U.S.	$90.00
Can.	$135.00
U.K.	£60.00

Top: Front view

THE VINERY

THE VINERY

TECHNICAL DATA

Designer:	Andrew Bill
Modeller:	Andrew Bill
Height:	4 ½", 11.9 cm
Colour:	White; pale pink and mauve roof; gold window and door frames
Issued:	1992 in a limited edition of 500
Variation:	Park Folly
Series:	Pastille Burners

PRICING DATA

U.S.	$250.00
Can.	$350.00
U.K.	£175.00

Top: Front view
Bottom: Back view

WATCHDOG CORNER

WATCHDOG CORNER

TECHNICAL DATA

Designer:	Unknown
Modeller:	Unknown
Height:	4", 10.1 cm
Colour:	White walls; pale pink roof; gold window and door frames; black dog
Issued:	1992 in a limited edition of 500
Series:	Pastille Burners

PRICING DATA

U.S.	$250.00
Can.	$350.00
U.K.	£175.00

Top: Front view
Centre: Back view
Bottom: Side view

THE WATERMILL

One can almost hear the rushing stream powering the wheel on this uniquely attractive house.

THE WATERMILL

TECHNICAL DATA

Designer:	Arnold Woolam
Modeller:	Arnold Woolam
Height:	4", 10.1 cm
Colour:	White; pale blue roof; yellow and brown wheel; brown chimney; green trim
Issued:	1980-1990

PRICING DATA

U.S.	$200.00
Can.	$275.00
U.K.	£140.00

Top: Front view
Bottom: Side view

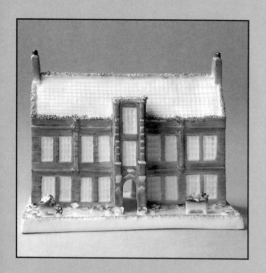

WILLBERFORCE HOUSE
HIGH STREET, HULL

This house was commissioned by Peter Jones in a limited edition of 500.

> Backstamp not
> available
> at press time

WILLBERFORCE HOUSE
HIGH STREET, HULL

TECHNICAL DATA

Designer:	Tony Sims
Modeller:	Tony Sims
Height:	4 ¾", 12.1 cm
Colour:	Brown walls; white roof and windows
Issued:	1982 in a limited edition of 500

PRICING DATA

U.S.	$250.00
Can.	$350.00
U.K.	£175.00

Top: Front view

THE WINDMILL

THE WINDMILL

TECHNICAL DATA

Designer:	Arnold Woolam
Modeller:	Arnold Woolam
Height:	5 ¼", 13.3 cm
Colour:	White walls with black beams; brown roof; white sails with black stripe in the centre; pink, blue and yellow flowers; green moss
Issued:	1979-1984

PRICING DATA

U.S.	$200.00
Can.	$300.00
U.K.	£135.00

Top: Front view
Centre: Back view
Bottom: Side view

EGG BOXES

EGG BOXES IN MING ROSE DESIGN

EGG BOXES
Handmade Flowers

ORCHIDS

TECHNICAL DATA

Designer:	Unknown
Size:	5" x 3", 12.7 x 7.6 cm
Colour:	White; purple and cream flowers
Issued:	1981

PRICING DATA

U.S.	$90.00
Can.	$125.00
U.K.	£60.00

ROSES

TECHNICAL DATA

Designer:	Unknown
Size:	5" x 3", 12.7 x 7.6 cm
Colour:	White; pink roses
Issued:	1981

PRICING DATA

U.S.	$90.00
Can.	$125.00
U.K.	£60.00

VIOLETS

TECHNICAL DATA

Designer:	Unknown
Size:	5" x 3", 12.7 x 7.6 cm
Colour:	White; purple violets
Issued:	1982

PRICING DATA

U.S.	$90.00
Can.	$125.00
U.K.	£60.00

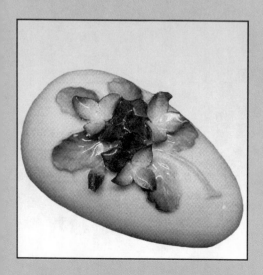

EGG BOXES

BIRDS

TECHNICAL DATA

Designer:	Unknown
Size:	Large: 5" x 3", 12.7 x 7.6 cm
	Small: 3 ½" x 2", 8.9 x 5.0 cm
Colour:	White; red, yellow and blue
	flowers; blue and green leaves
Issued:	c.1980

PRICING DATA

	Large	Small
U.S.	$90.00	$45.00
Can.	$125.00	$75.00
U.K.	£60.00	£30.00

MING ROSE

TECHNICAL DATA

Designer:	Unknown
Size:	Large: 5" x 3", 12.7 x 7.6 cm
	Small: 3 ½" x 2", 8.9 x 5.0 cm
Colour:	White, green and pink
Issued:	c.1980

PRICING DATA

	Large	Small
U.S.	$75.00	$35.00
Can.	$100.00	$50.00
U.K.	£50.00	£25.00

STRAWBERRY

TECHNICAL DATA

Designer:	Unknown
Size:	Large: 5" x 3", 12.7 x 7.6 cm
	Small: 3 ½" x 2", 8.9 x 5.0 cm
Colour:	White, red and green
Issued:	c.1980

PRICING DATA

	Large	Small
U.S.	$90.00	$45.00
Can.	$125.00	$75.00
U.K.	£60.00	£30.00

JEWELLED
ITEMS

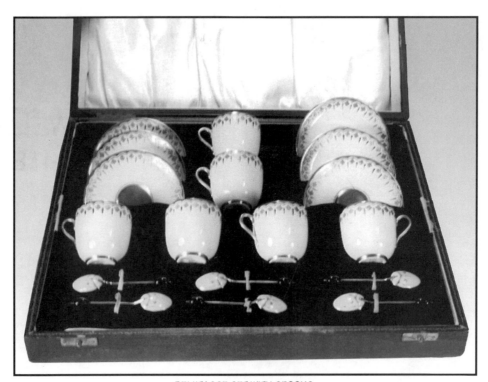

DEMITASSE SET WITH SPOONS

JEWELLED ITEMS AND MINIATURES

Cup and Saucer

Cup and Saucer

Cup and Saucer

Vase

Vase

Shoe

Sugar Bowl

Coffee Pot

Cream Jug

SHOES

The Pied Piper

Christmas Shoe

Aladdin

Frog Prince

Cinderella's Slipper

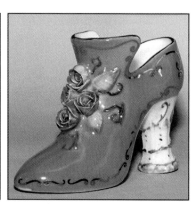

Sleeping Beauty's Shoe

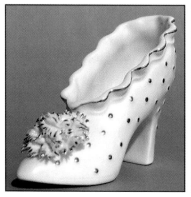

Wedding Shoe

Rose Cluster

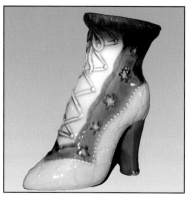

The Snow Queen

BUSTS AND HATS

Henrietta

Huntress

Ascot

Henley

Wimbledon

Derby

ALICE IN WONDERLAND

Queen

Alice

King

LITTLE GREY RABBIT

Birthday

Little Grey Rabbit's House

Fuzzypeg

CHILDREN'S COLLECTION

Duckling

Bear

Badger

PADDINGTON BEAR

On The Beach

Aunt Lucy

Reads a Book, First Version

Shopping, Second Version

Goes Fishing

Chimney Sweep, First Version

Tobogganing

32 Windsor Gardens, London
(Paddington Bear's Home)

In the Snow, Second Version

SLEEPING BEAUTY

Plate

Sleeping Beauty

Enchanted Castle

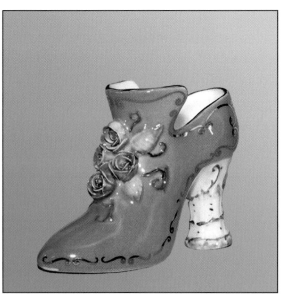

Sleeping Beauty's Shoe

CINDERELLA

Prince Charming

Cinderella

Pumpkin

Carriage

MINIATURES

Small Egg; Miniature Vase; Large Egg;
Teapot; Creamer and Sugar Bowl; Cup, Saucer and Plate; Wash Basin and Jug

Cup and Saucer (Imari)

Vase

Vase

CUPS AND SAUCERS

CUP AND SAUCER

TECHNICAL DATA

Pattern No.: 7162
Designer: Unknown
Height: Cup: 2 ¼", 5.7 cm
Diameter: Saucer: 4 ½", 11.9 cm
Colour: Turquoise, green and gold
Issued: 1880-1891

PRICING DATA

U.S. $500.00
Can. $700.00
U.K.   £350.00

CUP AND SAUCER

TECHNICAL DATA

Pattern No.: 3142
Designer: Unknown
Height: Cup: 2", 5.0 cm
Diameter: Saucer: 4 ½", 11.9 cm
Colour: Blue; burgundy; pink or yellow
Issued: 1891-1915

PRICING DATA

U.S. $350.00
Can. $500.00
U.K.   £250.00

CUP AND SAUCER

TECHNICAL DATA

Designer: Unknown
Height: Cup: 2", 5.0 cm
Diameter: Saucer: 3 ¾", 9.5 cm
Colour: Dark red with turquoise
             and white jewelling; gold
             interior
Issued: 1891-1939

PRICING DATA

U.S. $250.00
Can. $350.00
U.K.   £175.00

CUPS AND SAUCERS

CUP AND SAUCER

TECHNICAL DATA

Pattern No.: AD5720
Designer: Unknown
Height: Cup: 2 ¼", 5.7 cm
Diameter: Saucer: 4 ½", 11.9 cm
Colour: Gold and turquoise; cameos
Issued: 1891-1915

PRICING DATA

U.S. $700.00
Can. $950.00
U.K.   £475.00

CUP AND SAUCER

TECHNICAL DATA

Pattern No.: 7295
Designer: Unknown
Height: Cup: 2 ¼", 5.7 cm
Diameter: Saucer: 4 ½", 11.9 cm
Colour: Turquoise, green and gold;
            cameos
Issued: 1891-1915

PRICING DATA

U.S. $675.00
Can. $900.00
U.K.   £450.00

DEMITASSE CUP AND SAUCER

TECHNICAL DATA

Pattern No.: Unknown
Designer: Unknown
Height: Cup: 2", 5.0 cm
Diameter: Saucer: 3 ¾", 9.5 cm
Colour: Yellow and gold
Issued: c.1920

PRICING DATA

U.S. $225.00
Can. $275.00
U.K.   £135.00

MISCELLANEOUS ITEMS

SHOE

TECHNICAL DATA

Pattern No.: Unknown
Designer: Unknown
Size: 2" x 6", 5.0 x 15.0 cm
Colour: Gold, light blue and pink
Issued: Unknown

PRICING DATA

U.S. $1,500.00
Can. $2,000.00
U.K. £950.00

TRINKET BOX

TECHNICAL DATA

Pattern No.: V1504
Designer: Unknown
Diameter: 2 ½", 6.4 cm
Colour: Blue and gold
Issued: c.1891-1915

PRICING DATA

U.S. $300.00
Can. $425.00
U.K. £195.00

TWO-HANDLED DISH

TECHNICAL DATA

Pattern No.: Unknown
Designer: Unknown
Size: 2 ½" x 6", 6.4 x 15.0 cm
Colour: Burgundy with gold jewelling
Issued: Unknown

PRICING DATA

U.S. $200.00
Can. $275.00
U.K. £125.00

Note: See Miniature Section for further jewelled items.

MINIATURE COFFEE SET

MINIATURES

Vintage 1880-1930
Modern 1970-2000

MINIATURE JEWELLED VASES

VINTAGE

CUP AND SAUCER (Imari), Jewelled

TECHNICAL DATA

Pattern No.: Unknown
Modeller: Unknown
Height: Cup: 1 ½", 3.8 cm
Diameter: Saucer: 3 ½", 8.9 cm
Colour: Red, blue and gold
Issued: c.1880-1891

PRICING DATA

U.S. $175.00
Can. $250.00
U.K. £125.00

CUP AND SAUCER, Jewelled

TECHNICAL DATA

Pattern No.: B1842
Modeller: Unknown
Height: Cup: 1 ¾", 4.5 cm
Diameter: Saucer: 3 ¾", 9.5 cm
Colour: Pink and gold with pearl jewelling;
white and gold twist handle
Issued: 1880-1890

PRICING DATA

U.S. $350.00
Can. $500.00
U.K. £250.00

CUP AND SAUCER, Jewelled

TECHNICAL DATA

Pattern No.: A5897
Modeller: Unknown
Height: Cup: 1 ½", 3.8 cm
Diameter: Saucer: 2", 5.0 cm
Colour: Cobalt blue and gold
Issued: c.1891-1915

PRICING DATA

U.S. $300.00
Can. $425.00
U.K. £195.00

VINTAGE

CUP AND SAUCER, Jewelled

TECHNICAL DATA

Pattern No.: M5876
Modeller: Unknown
Height: Cup: 1", 2.5 cm
Diameter: Saucer: 2", 5.0 cm
Colour: Cobalt blue and gold
Issued: 1891-1915

PRICING DATA

U.S. $250.00
Can. $350.00
U.K. £175.00

CUP AND SAUCER, Jewelled

TECHNICAL DATA

Pattern No.: 6749
Modeller: Unknown
Height: Cup: 2", 5.0 cm
Diameter: Saucer: 2 ½", 6.4 cm
Colour: Cobalt blue and gold
Issued: 1891-1915

PRICING DATA

U.S. $250.00
Can. $350.00
U.K. £175.00

CUP AND SAUCER

TECHNICAL DATA

Pattern No.: Unknown
Modeller: Unknown
Height: Cup: 2", 5.0 cm
Diameter: Saucer: 2 ½", 6.4 cm
Colour: Cobalt blue, white and gold
with pink and yellow flowers
Issued: 1891-1915

PRICING DATA

U.S. $150.00
Can. $200.00
U.K. £100.00

VINTAGE

COFFEE POT, Jewelled

TECHNICAL DATA

Pattern No.: V7142
Designer: Unknown
Height: 2 ½", 6. 4 cm
Colour: Cobalt blue with gold jewels
Issued: 1891-1915

PRICING DATA

U.S. $575.00
Can. $850.00
U.K. £350.00

COVERED POT, Jewelled

TECHNICAL DATA

Pattern No.: V7142
Designer: Unknown
Height: 1 ¾", 4.5 cm
Colour: Cobalt blue with gold jewels
Issued: 1891-1915

PRICING DATA

U.S. $300.00
Can. $425.00
U.K. £195.00

CREAM JUG, Jewelled

TECHNICAL DATA

Pattern No.: V7142
Designer: Unknown
Height: 1 ½", 3.8 cm
Colour: Cobalt blue with gold jewels
Issued: 1891-1915

PRICING DATA

U.S. $250.00
Can. $300.00
U.K. £150.00

VINTAGE

SUGAR BOWL

TECHNICAL DATA

Pattern No.: V7142
Designer: Unknown
Height: ½", 1.2 cm
Colour: Cobalt blue with gold jewels
Issued: 1891-1915

PRICING DATA

U.S. $250.00
Can. $300.00
U.K. £150.00

CUP AND SAUCER (Indian Tree)

TECHNICAL DATA

Pattern No.: T4492
Modeller: Unknown
Height: Cup: 1 ¾", 4.5 cm
Diameter: Saucer: Unknown
Colour: White, green and pink
Issued: 1891-1915

PRICING DATA

U.S. $150.00
Can. $200.00
U.K. £100.00

TRAY (Indian Tree)

TECHNICAL DATA

Pattern No.: T4492
Modeller: Unknown
Length: 4 ½", 11.9 cm
Colour: White, green and pink
Issued: 1915-1949

PRICING DATA

U.S. $75.00
Can. $100.00
U.K. £50.00

VINTAGE

VASE, Jewelled

TECHNICAL DATA

Pattern No.: Y6043
Designer: Unknown
Height: 5 ¾", 14.6 cm
Colour: Cream and gilt with turquoise jewels
Issued: 1891-1915

PRICING DATA

U.S.	$975.00
Can.	$1,500.00
U.K.	£675.00

VASE, Jewelled

TECHNICAL DATA

Pattern No.: Unknown
Designer: Unknown
Height: 4", 10.1 cm
Colour: Green and gold with red jewelling
Issued: 1891-1915

PRICING DATA

U.S.	$750.00
Can.	$1,000.00
U.K.	£525.00

VASE

TECHNICAL DATA

Pattern No.: 7586
Designer: Unknown
Height: 4", 10.1 cm
Colour: Green and gold with pink floral cameo
Issued: 1891-1915

PRICING DATA

U.S.	$350.00
Can.	$500.00
U.K.	£250.00

VINTAGE

VASES (Pair), Jewelled

TECHNICAL DATA

Pattern No.:	Unknown
Designer:	Unknown
Height:	3 ½", 8.9 cm
Colour:	White; black bands with pearl jewelling; multicoloured floral design
Issued:	1880-1891

PRICING DATA

U.S.	$1,250.00
Can.	$1,750.00
U.K.	£850.00

Note: Priced as a pair.

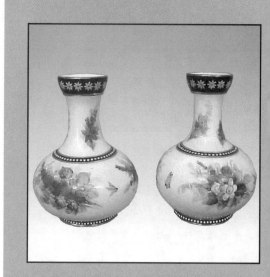

VASE

TECHNICAL DATA

Pattern No.:	A5272
Designer:	Unknown
Height:	3", 7.6 cm
Colour:	Gold with purple, pink and cream floral design
Issued:	1880-1891

PRICING DATA

U.S.	$700.00
Can.	$1,000.00
U.K.	£475.00

VASE (Four-handled)

TECHNICAL DATA

Pattern No.:	A8227
Designer:	Unknown
Height:	1 ½", 3.8 cm
Colour:	Pink and gold with multicoloured floral design
Issued:	1880-1891

PRICING DATA

U.S.	$650.00
Can.	$900.00
U.K.	£450.00

VINTAGE

TEAPOT

TECHNICAL DATA

Pattern No.: Unknown
Designer: Unknown
Height: 4 ½", 11.9 cm
Colour: White and cobalt blue
Issued: 1891-1915

PRICING DATA

U.S. $100.00
Can. $140.00
U.K.   £65.00

VASE (Two-handled), Jewelled

TECHNICAL DATA

Pattern No.: Unknown
Designer: Unknown
Height: 1 ½", 3.8 cm
Colour: Blue and gold; multicoloured
             cameo; pearl jewelling
Issued: 1891-1915

PRICING DATA

U.S. $500.00
Can. $700.00
U.K.   £350.00

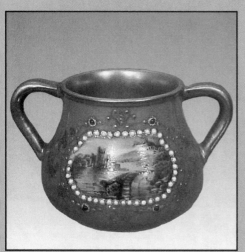

MODERN

Coalbrookdale

Description	Size	U.S. $	Can. $	U.K. £
Candle snuffer	—	70.00	100.00	45.00
Cream jug	1 ½"	80.00	115.00	55.00
Cup	¾"	50.00	75.00	35.00
Mug	—	100.00	150.00	65.00
Plate	3"	50.00	75.00	35.00
Saucer	2 ¼"	50.00	75.00	35.00
Sugar	1 ½"	100.00	150.00	65.00
Tea pot	2"	120.00	175.00	80.00
Wash basin	2 ¾"	50.00	75.00	35.00
Wash jug	2 ¾"	100.00	150.00	65.00
Boxed sets				
Teapot, cream, sugar		325.00	475.00	215.00
Cup, saucer, plate		175.00	250.00	115.00

Hong Kong

Description	Size	U.S. $	Can. $	U.K. £
Candle snuffer	—	55.00	80.00	37.00
Cream jug	1 ½"	60.00	85.00	40.00
Cup	¾"	37.50	55.00	25.00
Mug	—	75.00	110.00	50.00
Plate	3"	37.50	55.00	25.00
Saucer	2 ¼"	37.50	55.00	25.00
Sugar	1 ½"	75.00	110.00	50.00
Tea pot	2"	90.00	130.00	60.00
Wash basin	2 ¾"	37.50	55.00	25.00
Wash jug	2 ¾"	75.00	110.00	50.00
Boxed sets				
Teapot, cream, sugar		240.00	350.00	160.00
Cup, saucer, plate		130.00	185.00	85.00

Indian Tree (Traditional)

Description	Size	U.S. $	Can. $	U.K. £
Candle snuffer	—	45.00	65.00	30.00
Cream jug	1 ½"	50.00	75.00	35.00
Cup	¾"	30.00	45.00	20.00
Mug	—	65.00	95.00	45.00
Plate	3"	30.00	45.00	20.00
Saucer	2 ¼"	30.00	45.00	20.00
Sugar	1 ½"	65.00	95.00	45.00
Tea pot	2"	75.00	110.00	50.00
Wash basin	2 ¾"	30.00	45.00	20.00
Wash jug	2 ¾"	75.00	110.00	50.00
Boxed sets				
Teapot, cream, sugar		200.00	300.00	135.00
Cup, saucer, plate		100.00	150.00	65.00

MODERN

Indian Tree (Coral)

Description	Size	U.S. $	Can. $	U.K. £
Candle snuffer	—	47.50	70.00	30.00
Cream jug	1 ½"	55.00	80.00	37.00
Cup	¾"	35.00	50.00	25.00
Mug	—	67.50	95.00	45.00
Plate	3"	35.00	50.00	25.00
Saucer	2 ¼"	35.00	50.00	25.00
Sugar	1 ½"	67.50	95.00	45.00
Tea pot	2"	80.00	115.00	55.00
Wash basin	2 ¾"	35.00	50.00	25.00
Wash jug	2 ¾"	67.50	95.00	45.00
Boxed sets				
Teapot, cream, sugar		210.00	300.00	140.00
Cup, saucer, plate		115.00	165.00	75.00

Photograph not available at press time

Leighton Sprays

Description	Size	U.S. $	Can. $	U.K. £
Candle snuffer	—	60.00	90.00	60.00
Cream jug	1 ½"	70.00	100.00	47.00
Cup	¾"	45.00	65.00	30.00
Mug	—	90.00	130.00	60.00
Plate	3"	45.00	65.00	30.00
Saucer	2 ¼"	45.00	65.00	30.00
Sugar	1 ½"	90.00	130.00	60.00
Tea pot	2"	105.00	150.00	70.00
Wash basin	2 ¾"	45.00	65.00	30.00
Wash jug	2 ¾"	90.00	130.00	60.00
Boxed sets				
Teapot, cream, sugar		275.00	400.00	185.00
Cup, saucer, plate		150.00	215.00	100.00

Ming Rose

Description	Size	U.S. $	Can. $	U.K. £
Candle Snuffer	—	35.00	50.00	25.00
Cream jug	1 ½"	40.00	60.00	28.00
Cup	¾"	25.00	35.00	17.00
Mug	—	50.00	75.00	35.00
Plate	3"	25.00	35.00	17.00
Saucer	2 ¼"	25.00	35.00	17.00
Sugar	1 ½"	50.00	75.00	35.00
Tea pot	2"	60.00	85.00	40.00
Wash basin	2 ¾"	25.00	35.00	17.00
Wash jug	2 ¾"	50.00	75.00	35.00
Boxed sets				
Teapot, cream, sugar		160.00	230.00	110.00
Cup, saucer, plate		85.00	125.00	55.00

MODERN

Pageant

Description	Size	U.S. $	Can. $	U.K. £
Cream jug	1 ½"	60.00	90.00	60.00
Cup	¾"	37.50	55.00	25.00
Mug	—	75.00	110.00	50.00
Plate	3"	37.50	55.00	25.00
Saucer	2 ¼"	37.50	55.00	25.00
Sugar	1 ½"	75.00	110.00	50.00
Tea pot	2"	90.00	135.00	60.00
Wash basin	2 ¾"	37.50	55.00	25.00
Wash jug	2 ¾"	75.00	110.00	50.00
Boxed sets				
Teapot, cream, sugar		240.00	350.00	160.00
Cup, saucer, plate		130.00	190.00	85.00

Shrewsbury

Description	Size	U.S. $	Can. $	U.K. £
Cream jug	1 ½"	60.00	90.00	60.00
Cup	¾"	37.50	55.00	25.00
Mug	—	75.00	110.00	50.00
Plate	3"	37.50	55.00	25.00
Saucer	2 ¼"	37.50	55.00	25.00
Sugar	1 ½"	75.00	110.00	50.00
Tea pot	2"	90.00	135.00	60.00
Wash basin	2 ¾"	37.50	55.00	25.00
Wash jug	2 ¾"	75.00	110.00	50.00
Boxed sets				
Teapot, cream, sugar		240.00	350.00	160.00
Cup, saucer, plate		130.00	190.00	85.00

Strawberry

Description	Size	U.S. $	Can. $	U.K. £
Cream jug	1 ½"	60.00	90.00	60.00
Cup	¾"	37.50	55.00	25.00
Mug	—	75.00	110.00	50.00
Plate	3"	37.50	55.00	25.00
Saucer	2 ¼"	37.50	55.00	25.00
Sugar	1 ½"	75.00	110.00	50.00
Tea pot	2"	90.00	135.00	60.00
Wash basin	2 ¾"	37.50	55.00	25.00
Wash jug	2 ¾"	75.00	110.00	50.00
Boxed sets				
Teapot, cream, sugar		240.00	350.00	160.00
Cup, saucer, plate		130.00	190.00	85.00

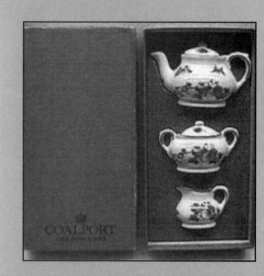

MODERN

Tulip Tree

Description	Size	U.S. $	Can. $	U.K. £
Cream jug	1 ½"	70.00	100.00	47.00
Cup	¾"	45.00	65.00	30.00
Mug	—	90.00	130.00	60.00
Plate	3"	45.00	65.00	30.00
Saucer	2 ¼"	45.00	65.00	30.00
Sugar	1 ½"	90.00	130.00	60.00
Tea pot	2"	105.00	150.00	70.00
Wash basin	2 ¾"	45.00	65.00	30.00
Wash jug	2 ¾"	90.00	130.00	60.00
Boxed sets				
Teapot, cream, sugar		275.00	400.00	185.00
Cup, saucer, plate		150.00	215.00	100.00

Willow (Blue)

Description	Size	U.S. $	Can. $	U.K. £
Candle snuffer	—	45.00	65.00	30.00
Cream jug	1 ½"	50.00	75.00	35.00
Cup	¾"	30.00	45.00	20.00
Mug	—	65.00	95.00	45.00
Pitcher	1 ¾"	50.00	75.00	35.00
Plate	3"	30.00	45.00	20.00
Saucer	2 ¼"	30.00	45.00	20.00
Sugar	1 ½"	65.00	95.00	45.00
Tea pot	2"	75.00	110.00	50.00
Wash basin	2 ¾"	30.00	45.00	20.00
Wash jug	2 ¾"	75.00	110.00	50.00
Boxed sets				
Teapot, cream, sugar		200.00	300.00	135.00
Cup, saucer, plate		100.00	150.00	65.00

Willow (Coral)

Description	Size	U.S. $	Can. $	U.K. £
Candle snuffer	—	47.50	70.00	30.00
Cream jug	1 ½"	55.00	80.00	37.00
Cup	¾"	35.00	50.00	25.00
Mug	—	67.50	95.00	45.00
Plate	3"	35.00	50.00	25.00
Saucer	2 ¼"	35.00	50.00	25.00
Sugar	1 ½"	67.50	95.00	45.00
Tea pot	2"	80.00	115.00	55.00
Wash basin	2 ¾"	35.00	50.00	25.00
Wash jug	2 ¾"	67.50	95.00	45.00
Boxed sets				
Teapot, cream, sugar		210.00	300.00	140.00
Cup, saucer, plate		115.00	165.00	75.00

MODERN

Willow (Green)

Description	Size	U.S. $	Can. $	U.K. £
Candle snuffer	—	47.50	70.00	30.00
Cream jug	1 ½"	55.00	80.00	37.00
Cup	¾"	35.00	50.00	25.00
Mug	—	67.50	95.00	45.00
Plate	3"	35.00	50.00	25.00
Saucer	2 ¼"	35.00	50.00	25.00
Sugar	1 ½"	67.50	95.00	45.00
Tea pot	2"	80.00	115.00	55.00
Wash basin	2 ¾"	35.00	50.00	25.00
Wash jug	2 ¾"	67.50	95.00	45.00
Boxed sets				
Teapot, cream, sugar		210.00	300.00	140.00
Cup, saucer, plate		115.00	165.00	75.00

VASE (Ming Rose)

TECHNICAL DATA

Designer:	Unknown
Height:	3", 7.6 cm
Colour:	Red, yellow and blue flowers
Issued:	Unknown

PRICING DATA

U.S.	$30.00
Can.	$45.00
U.K.	£20.00

PLATE (No. 13)

TECHNICAL DATA

Designer:	Unknown
Diameter:	3", 7.6 cm
Colour:	Green trees and grass; brown fence; grey sheep
Issued:	Unknown

PRICING DATA

U.S.	$15.00
Can.	$20.00
U.K.	£10.00

NOVELTY ITEMS

Busts
Hats
Shoes

HENRIETTA

BUSTS

HENRIETTA

TECHNICAL DATA

Designer:	John Bromley
Modeller:	John Bromley
Height:	6", 15.0 cm
Colour:	Fleshtone; pale blue and pink dress; straw hat with dark blue ribbon and pink and yellow roses; maroon ribbon
Issued:	1982 in a limited edition of 100

PRICING DATA

U.S.	$150.00
Can.	$225.00
U.K.	£100.00

HUNTRESS

TECHNICAL DATA

Designer:	John Bromley
Modeller:	John Bromley
Height:	8 ¾", 22.2 cm
Colour:	Dark grey hat with blue band, brown feather and purple ribbon; chestnut brown jacket; white cravat trimmed with pink and blue
Issued:	1982 in a limited edition of 100

PRICING DATA

U.S.	$150.00
Can.	$225.00
U.K.	£100.00

BUSTS

LORD BADEN-POWELL

TECHNICAL DATA

Designer:	John Bromley
Modeller:	John Bromley
Height:	Unknown
Colour:	White
Issued:	1985

PRICING DATA

U.S.	$75.00
Can.	$125.00
U.K.	£50.00

YOUNG GIRL

TECHNICAL DATA

Designer:	John Bromley
Modeller:	John Bromley
Height:	6", 15.0 cm
Colour:	Fleshtone; light brown hair; green hat with pink and yellow flowers; white collar and cuffs; blue ring
Issued:	1982 in a limited edition of 100
Series:	Art Deco

PRICING DATA

U.S.	$150.00
Can.	$225.00
U.K.	£100.00

HATS

ASCOT

TECHNICAL DATA

Designer:	Sharon Wells
Modeller:	Jenny Oliver
Height:	3", 7.6 cm
Colour:	Dark beige hat, paler beige feather; dark brown band and bows
Issued:	1998-2000
Series:	Precious Collections - Hats

PRICING DATA

U.S.	$85.00
Can.	$125.00
U.K.	£55.00

DERBY

TECHNICAL DATA

Designer:	Sharon Wells
Modeller:	Jenny Oliver
Height:	4 ¼", 10.8 cm
Colour:	Beige hat with blue stripes and polka dots; beige and blue fan; beige purse with blue polka dots and bow
Issued:	1998-2000
Series:	Precious Collections - Hats

PRICING DATA

U.S.	$85.00
Can.	$125.00
U.K.	£55.00

HATS

HENLEY

TECHNICAL DATA

Designer:	Sharon Wells
Modeller:	Jenny Oliver
Height:	4", 10.1 cm
Colour:	Beige straw hat with multicoloured handmade flowers; cream gloves
Issued:	1998-2000
Series:	Precious Collections - Hats

PRICING DATA

U.S.	$100.00
Can.	$140.00
U.K.	£60.00

WIMBLEDON

TECHNICAL DATA

Designer:	Sharon Wells
Modeller:	Jenny Oliver
Height:	4 ¼", 10.8 cm
Colour:	Pink; deep pink rose and strawberries; cream gloves
Issued:	1998-2000
Series:	Precious Collections - Hats

PRICING DATA

U.S.	$75.00
Can.	$125.00
U.K.	£50.00

SHOES

ALADDIN

TECHNICAL DATA

Designer:	Sue McGarrigle
Modeller:	Jenny Oliver
Length:	4", 10.1 cm
Colour:	Yellow, purple, gold and white
Issued:	1999 to the present
Series:	Precious Collections - Shoes

PRICING DATA

U.S.	$ —
Can.	$ —
U.K.	£39.00

CHRISTMAS SHOE

TECHNICAL DATA

Modeller:	Unknown
Length:	4", 10.1 cm
Colour:	White shoe decorated with holly, berries, flower; purple heel and front
Issued:	1994

PRICING DATA

U.S.	$60.00
Can.	$90.00
U.K.	£35.00

Note: Commissioned by Compton & Woodhouse.

CINDERELLA'S SLIPPER

TECHNICAL DATA

Designer:	Sue McGarrigle
Modeller:	Jenny Oliver
Length:	3 ¼", 8.3 cm
Colour:	Ivory mother-of-pearl lustre; pink roses; green leaves on toe of shoe; black and gold clock on back of shoe; brown edging
Issued:	1999 to the present
Series:	1. Cinderella
	2. Precious Collections - Shoes

PRICING DATA

U.S.	$ —
Can.	$ —
U.K.	£39.00

SHOES

FROG PRINCE

TECHNICAL DATA

Designer:	Sue McGarrigle
Modeller:	Jenny Oliver
Length:	3 ¾", 9.5 cm
Colour:	Green, emerald green and gold
Issued:	1999 to the present
Series:	Precious Collections - Shoes

PRICING DATA

U.S.	$ —
Can.	$ —
U.K.	£39.00

THE PIED PIPER

TECHNICAL DATA

Designer:	Sue McGarrigle
Modeller:	Jenny Oliver
Length:	3 ¾", 9.5 cm
Colour:	Yellow; red mice and diamonds; white band with black musical notes; blue flute
Issued:	1999 to the present
Series:	Precious Collections - Shoes

PRICING DATA

U.S.	$ —
Can.	$ —
U.K.	£39.00

ROSE CLUSTER

TECHNICAL DATA

Modeller:	Unknown
Length:	4 ¼", 10.8 cm
Colour:	White shoe decorated with pink roses, green leaves and gold highlights; pink heel
Issued:	1994

PRICING DATA

U.S.	$60.00
Can.	$90.00
U.K.	£35.00

Note: Commissioned by Compton & Woodhouse.

SHOES

SLEEPING BEAUTY'S SHOE

TECHNICAL DATA

Designer:	Sue McGarrigle
Modeller:	Jenny Oliver
Length:	3 ½", 8.9 cm
Colour:	Rose-pink shoe with pink roses, green leaves and gold trim; pink heel with rose-pink trim
Issued:	1999 to the present
Series:	1. Precious Collections - Shoes
	2. Sleeping Beauty

PRICING DATA

U.S.	$ —
Can.	$ —
U.K.	£39.00

THE SNOW QUEEN

TECHNICAL DATA

Designer:	Sue McGarrigle
Modeller:	Jenny Oliver
Length:	3 ¼", 8.3 cm
Colour:	Cream, grey and white boot
Issued:	1999 to the present
Series:	Precious Collections - Shoes

PRICING DATA

U.S.	$ —
Can.	$ —
U.K.	£39.00

WEDDING SHOE

TECHNICAL DATA

Modeller:	Unknown
Length:	3 ½", 8.9 cm
Colour:	Cream shoe with gold highlights
Issued:	1994

PRICING DATA

U.S.	$60.00
Can.	$90.00
U.K.	£35.00

Note: Commissioned by Compton & Woodhouse.

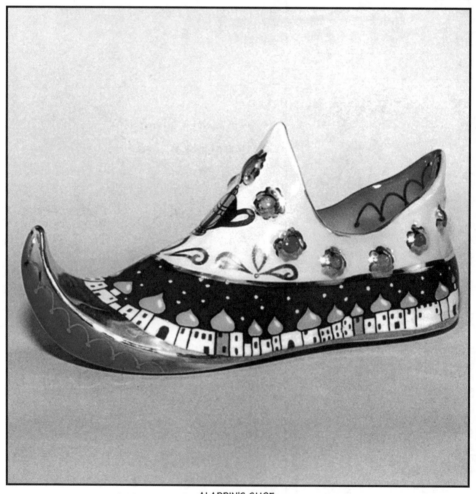

ALADDIN'S SHOE

ROYAL
COMMEMORATIVES

40TH ANNIVERSARY PLATE

ROYAL COMMEMORATIVES

JUBILEE BOWL
Silver Jubilee of Her Majesty Queen Elizabeth II

TECHNICAL DATA

Designer:	Unknown
Diameter:	10 ¼", 26.0 cm
Colour:	White; pink roses, gold leaves
Issued:	1977

PRICING DATA

U.S.	$200.00
Can.	$300.00
U.K.	£135.00

ANNIVERSARY GOBLET
40th Anniversary of the Accession of H.M. Queen Elizabeth II

TECHNICAL DATA

Designer:	Unknown
Height:	4 ½", 11.9 cm
Colour:	Ruby and gold
Issued:	1992 in a limited edition of 2,000

PRICING DATA

U.S.	$50.00
Can.	$70.00
U.K.	£35.00

ANNIVERSARY PLATE
40th Anniversary of the Accession of H.M. Queen Elizabeth II

TECHNICAL DATA

Designer:	Unknown
Diameter:	10 ½", 26.7 cm
Colour:	Ruby background; yellow daffodils, peach roses, mauve thistles; green shamrocks; black and white cameos
Issued:	1992 in a limited edition of 5,000

PRICING DATA

U.S.	$75.00
Can.	$100.00
U.K.	£50.00

ROYAL COMMEMORATIVES

BIRTHDAY GOBLET
The Sixtieth Birthday of
H.M. Queen Elizabeth II

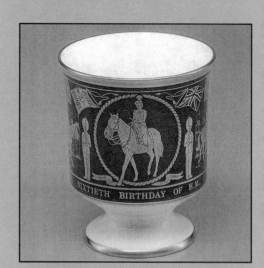

TECHNICAL DATA

Designer:	Unknown
Size:	3" x 3", 7.6 x 7.6 cm
Colour:	White, black and gold
Issued:	1986 in a limited edition of 2,000

PRICING DATA

U.S.	$50.00
Can.	$70.00
U.K.	£35.00

CHALICE
Investiture of Prince Charles

"Charles Prince of Wales presented to the people by Queen Elizabeth, Caernarvon Castle July 1st 1969", written on chalice.

TECHNICAL DATA

Designer:	Unknown
Size:	3" x 3", 7.6 x 7.6 cm
Colour:	White and gold
Issued:	1969

PRICING DATA

U.S.	$75.00
Can.	$100.00
U.K.	£50.00

ROYAL VASE
Marriage of Prince Charles and
Lady Diana Spencer

TECHNICAL DATA

Designer:	Unknown
Height:	6 ½", 16.5 cm
Colour:	White; handmade pink roses and green leaves; Westminster Abbey; crown atop lid
Issued:	1981

PRICING DATA

U.S.	$500.00
Can.	$700.00
U.K.	£350.00

STORYBOOK

Alice in Wonderland
Basil Brush
Children's Collection
Cinderella
Little Grey Rabbit
Paddington Bear
Postman Pat
Sleeping Beauty

CINDERELLA'S CARRIAGE

ALICE IN WONDERLAND

ALICE

TECHNICAL DATA

Designer: Unknown
Modeller: Margaret Whitaker
Height: 4 ¾", 12.1 cm
Colour: Blue dress and hair ribbon; white petticoat; purple shoes and book cover; blonde hair
Issued: 1975-1980

PRICING DATA

U.S. $150.00
Can. $225.00
U.K. £100.00

CHESHIRE CAT

TECHNICAL DATA

Designer: Unknown
Modeller: Margaret Whitaker
Height: 2", 5.0 cm
Colour: Chestnut with dark brown markings
Issued: 1975-1980

PRICING DATA

U.S. $150.00
Can. $225.00
U.K. £100.00

COOK

TECHNICAL DATA

Designer: Unknown
Modeller: Margaret Whitaker
Height: 5 ½", 14.0 cm
Colour: White apron and cap; grey dress and ribbon on cap; yellow pepper pot
Issued: 1975-1980

PRICING DATA

U.S. $150.00
Can. $225.00
U.K. £100.00

ALICE IN WONDERLAND

DODO

TECHNICAL DATA

Designer:	Unknown
Modeller:	Margaret Whitaker
Height:	5", 12.7 cm
Colour:	Green and yellow bird
Issued:	1975-1980

PRICING DATA

U.S.	$150.00
Can.	$225.00
U.K.	£100.00

DORMOUSE

TECHNICAL DATA

Designer:	Unknown
Modeller:	Margaret Whitaker
Height:	3 ½", 8.9 cm
Colour:	Brown dormouse; black and white striped bowl
Issued:	1975-1980

PRICING DATA

U.S.	$150.00
Can.	$225.00
U.K.	£100.00

DUCHESS

TECHNICAL DATA

Designer:	Unknown
Modeller:	Margaret Whitaker
Height:	6 ½", 16.5 cm
Colour:	Yellow dress; red coat trimmed with blue; yellow, white and blue hat; pale brown shoes
Issued:	1975-1980

PRICING DATA

U.S.	$150.00
Can.	$225.00
U.K.	£100.00

ALICE IN WONDERLAND

GARDENER

TECHNICAL DATA

Designer:	Unknown
Modeller:	Margaret Whitaker
Height:	5 ½", 14.0 cm
Colour:	White tunic with black 'spade' design; red collar, sleeves, cap and paint brush; yellow boots; cream can
Issued:	1975-1980

PRICING DATA

U.S.	$150.00
Can.	$225.00
U.K.	£100.00

HATTER

TECHNICAL DATA

Designer:	Unknown
Modeller:	Margaret Whitaker
Height:	6 ½", 16.5 cm
Colour:	Pink jacket; yellow waistcoat; yellow bow tie with red spots; grey trousers; white hat; brown shoes
Issued:	1975-1980

PRICING DATA

U.S.	$150.00
Can.	$225.00
U.K.	£100.00

KING

TECHNICAL DATA

Designer:	Unknown
Modeller:	Margaret Whitaker
Height:	5 ½", 14.0 cm
Colour:	Blue cloak with ermine trim; red and yellow outfit and crown; pale brown shoes
Issued:	1975-1980

PRICING DATA

U.S.	$150.00
Can.	$225.00
U.K.	£100.00

ALICE IN WONDERLAND

KNAVE OF HEARTS

TECHNICAL DATA

Designer:	Unknown
Modeller:	Margaret Whitaker
Height:	5", 12.7 cm
Colour:	Red, yellow and blue clothing; white and red hat; black shoes with yellow buckles; beige tray of tarts
Issued:	1975-1980

PRICING DATA

U.S.	$150.00
Can.	$225.00
U.K.	£100.00

QUEEN

TECHNICAL DATA

Designer:	Unknown
Modeller:	Margaret Whitaker
Height:	6", 15.0 cm
Colour:	Red, yellow and blue dress; blue and yellow cap
Issued:	1975-1980

PRICING DATA

U.S.	$150.00
Can.	$225.00
U.K.	£100.00

WHITE RABBIT

TECHNICAL DATA

Designer:	Unknown
Modeller:	Margaret Whitaker
Height:	3", 7.6 cm
Colour:	White rabbit; blue jacket; green waistcoat and bow tie; beige and white clock
Issued:	1975-1980

PRICING DATA

U.S.	$150.00
Can.	$225.00
U.K.	£100.00

BASIL BRUSH

BASIL AND HIS STORY

TECHNICAL DATA

Designer: Unknown
Modeller: Catherine Barnsley
Height: 4 ¼", 10.8 cm
Colour: Dark blue jacket; maroon
                waistcoat; green cravat;
                white and black book pages
Issued: 1975-1980

PRICING DATA

U.S. $75.00
Can. $100.00
U.K.   £50.00

BASIL AT BEDTIME

TECHNICAL DATA

Designer: Unknown
Modeller: Catherine Barnsley
Height: 4 ¼", 10.8 cm
Colour: Orange dressing gown; green
                cravat and night cap; red hot
                water bottle
Issued: 1975-1980

PRICING DATA

U.S. $75.00
Can. $100.00
U.K.   £50.00

BASIL BRUSH

TECHNICAL DATA

Designer: Unknown
Modeller: Margaret Whitaker
Height: 4 ¼", 10.8 cm
Colour: Dark blue coat; maroon
                waistcoat; green cravat
Issued: 1975-1980

PRICING DATA

U.S. $75.00
Can. $100.00
U.K.   £50.00

BASIL BRUSH

BASIL THE ARTIST

TECHNICAL DATA

Designer:	Unknown
Modeller:	Margaret Whitaker
Height:	4 ¼", 10.8 cm
Colour:	Blue coat; white neck tie with red polka dots; dark blue cap; white palette with coloured paints
Issued:	1975-1980

PRICING DATA

U.S.	$75.00
Can.	$100.00
U.K.	£50.00

BASIL BRUSH MONEY BOX

TECHNICAL DATA

Designer:	Unknown
Modeller:	Margaret Whitaker
Height:	4 ¼", 10.8 cm
Colour:	Unknown
Issued:	c.1975

PRICING DATA

U.S.	$75.00
Can.	$100.00
U.K.	£50.00

Photograph not available at press time

CHILDREN'S COLLECTION

BADGER

TECHNICAL DATA

Modeller:	Margaret Whitaker
Height:	2 ¼", 5.7 cm
Colour:	White; facial features outlined in brown
Issued:	1975-1982

PRICING DATA

U.S.	$30.00
Can.	$45.00
U.K.	£20.00

BEAGLE

TECHNICAL DATA

Modeller:	Margaret Whitaker
Height:	3", 7.6 cm
Colour:	White; facial features outlined in brown
Issued:	1975-1982

PRICING DATA

U.S.	$30.00
Can.	$45.00
U.K.	£20.00

BEAR

TECHNICAL DATA

Modeller:	Margaret Whitaker
Height:	3 ¾", 9.5 cm
Colour:	White; facial features outlined in brown
Issued:	1975-1982

PRICING DATA

U.S.	$30.00
Can.	$45.00
U.K.	£20.00

CHILDREN'S COLLECTION

CAT

TECHNICAL DATA

Modeller: Margaret Whitaker
Height: 1 ½", 3.8 cm
Colour: White; facial features outlined
             in brown
Issued: 1975-1982

PRICING DATA

U.S. $40.00
Can. $60.00
U.K.   £25.00

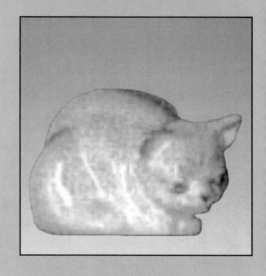

DEER

TECHNICAL DATA

Modeller: Margaret Whitaker
Height: 2 ½", 6.4 cm
Colour: White; facial features outlined
             in brown
Issued: 1975-1982

PRICING DATA

U.S. $40.00
Can. $60.00
U.K.   £25.00

DONKEY

TECHNICAL DATA

Modeller: Margaret Whitaker
Height: 3 ¼", 8.3 cm
Colour: White; facial features outlined
             in brown
Issued: 1975-1982

PRICING DATA

U.S. $30.00
Can. $45.00
U.K.   £20.00

CHILDREN'S COLLECTION

DUCKLING

TECHNICAL DATA

Modeller:	Margaret Whitaker
Height:	3", 7.6 cm
Colour:	White; facial features outlined in brown
Issued:	1975-1982

PRICING DATA

U.S.	$30.00
Can.	$45.00
U.K.	£20.00

FOAL

TECHNICAL DATA

Modeller:	Margaret Whitaker
Height:	2", 5.0 cm
Colour:	White; facial features outlined in brown
Issued:	1975-1982

PRICING DATA

U.S.	$45.00
Can.	$65.00
U.K.	£30.00

Photograph not
available
at press time

FOX

TECHNICAL DATA

Modeller:	Margaret Whitaker
Height:	1 ½", 3.8 cm
Colour:	White; facial features outlined in brown
Issued:	1975-1982

PRICING DATA

U.S.	$40.00
Can.	$60.00
U.K.	£25.00

CHILDREN'S COLLECTION

FROG

TECHNICAL DATA

Modeller: Margaret Whitaker
Height: 2 ¼", 5.7 cm
Colour: White; facial features outlined
            in brown
Issued: 1975-1982

PRICING DATA

U.S. $40.00
Can. $60.00
U.K.   £25.00

HAMSTER

TECHNICAL DATA

Modeller: Margaret Whitaker
Height: 2 ½", 6.4 cm
Colour: White; facial features outlined
            in brown
Issued: 1975-1982

PRICING DATA

U.S. $30.00
Can. $45.00
U.K.   £20.00

HEDGEHOG

TECHNICAL DATA

Modeller: Margaret Whitaker
Height: 2 ½", 6.4 cm
Colour: White; facial features outlined
            in brown
Issued: 1975-1982

PRICING DATA

U.S. $30.00
Can. $45.00
U.K.   £20.00

CHILDREN'S COLLECTION

HIPPOPOTAMUS

TECHNICAL DATA

Modeller:	Margaret Whitaker
Height:	1 ¾'", 4.4 cm
Colour:	White; facial features outlined in brown
Issued:	1975-1982

PRICING DATA

U.S.	$40.00
Can.	$65.00
U.K.	£25.00

HORSE

TECHNICAL DATA

Modeller:	Margaret Whitaker
Height:	3", 7.6 cm
Colour:	White; facial features outlined in brown
Issued:	1975-1982

PRICING DATA

U.S.	$45.00
Can.	$65.00
U.K.	£30.00

MOUSE

TECHNICAL DATA

Modeller:	Margaret Whitaker
Height:	2 ¼", 5.7 cm
Colour:	White; facial features outlined in brown
Issued:	1975-1982

PRICING DATA

U.S.	$30.00
Can.	$45.00
U.K.	£20.00

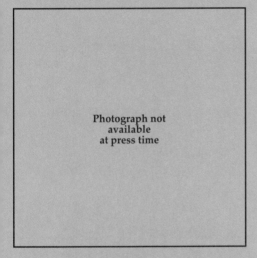

Photograph not available at press time

CHILDREN'S COLLECTION

OWL

TECHNICAL DATA

Modeller:	Margaret Whitaker
Height:	2 ¼", 5.7 cm
Colour:	White; facial features outlined in brown
Issued:	1975-1982

PRICING DATA

U.S.	$30.00
Can.	$45.00
U.K.	£20.00

PELICAN

TECHNICAL DATA

Modeller:	Margaret Whitaker
Height:	2", 5.0 cm
Colour:	White; facial features outlined in brown
Issued:	1975-1982

PRICING DATA

U.S.	$40.00
Can.	$60.00
U.K.	£25.00

Photograph not available at press time

PENGUIN

TECHNICAL DATA

Modeller:	Margaret Whitaker
Height:	3 ¾", 9.5 cm
Colour:	White; facial features outlined in brown
Issued:	1975-1982

PRICING DATA

U.S.	$40.00
Can.	$60.00
U.K.	£25.00

CHILDREN'S COLLECTION

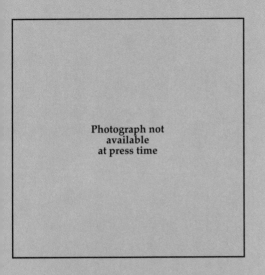

PUFFIN

TECHNICAL DATA

Modeller:	Margaret Whitaker
Height:	3", 7.6 cm
Colour:	White; facial features outlined in brown
Issued:	1975-1982

PRICING DATA

U.S.	$40.00
Can.	$60.00
U.K.	£25.00

RABBIT

TECHNICAL DATA

Modeller:	Margaret Whitaker
Height:	2 ½", 6.4 cm
Colour:	White; facial features outlined in brown
Issued:	1975-1982

PRICING DATA

U.S.	$30.00
Can.	$45.00
U.K.	£20.00

RAM

TECHNICAL DATA

Modeller:	Margaret Whitaker
Height:	2", 5.0 cm
Colour:	White; facial features outlined in brown
Issued:	1975-1982

PRICING DATA

U.S.	$30.00
Can.	$45.00
U.K.	£20.00

CHILDREN'S COLLECTION

SEAL

TECHNICAL DATA

Modeller: Margaret Whitaker
Size: 1 ¾" x 4 ¼", 4.5 x 10.8 cm
Colour: White; facial features outlined in brown
Issued: 1975-1982

PRICING DATA

U.S. $30.00
Can. $45.00
U.K. £20.00

SNAIL

TECHNICAL DATA

Modeller: Margaret Whitaker
Height: 3", 7.6 cm
Colour: White; facial features outlined in brown
Issued: 1975-1982

PRICING DATA

U.S. $40.00
Can. $60.00
U.K. £25.00

SQUIRREL

TECHNICAL DATA

Modeller: Margaret Whitaker
Height: 2 ¾", 7.0 cm
Colour: White; facial features outlined in brown
Issued: 1975-1982

PRICING DATA

U.S. $30.00
Can. $45.00
U.K. £20.00

CHILDREN'S COLLECTION

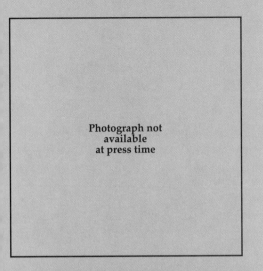

Photograph not
available
at press time

TAWNY OWL

TECHNICAL DATA

Modeller:	Margaret Whitaker
Height:	2 ¾", 7.0 cm
Colour:	White; facial features outlined in brown
Issued:	1975-1982

PRICING DATA

U.S.	$40.00
Can.	$60.00
U.K.	£25.00

TORTOISE

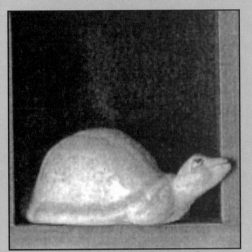

TECHNICAL DATA

Modeller:	Margaret Whitaker
Height:	1 ½", 3.8 cm
Colour:	White; facial features outlined in brown
Issued:	1975-1982

PRICING DATA

U.S.	$30.00
Can.	$45.00
U.K.	£20.00

CINDERELLA

CARRIAGE

TECHNICAL DATA

Designer:	Sue McGarrigle
Modeller:	Jenny Oliver
Height:	3 ½", 9.0 cm
Colour:	Orange carriage; brown, white and green wheels; purple curtains; green leaves; pink mice
Issued:	1999 to the present

PRICING DATA

U.S.	$ —
Can.	$ —
U.K.	£49.00

Note: The 'Carriage' has a removable lid.

CINDERELLA

TECHNICAL DATA

Designer:	Sue McGarrigle
Modeller:	Jack Glynn
Height:	8 ½", 21.5 cm
Colour:	White gown trimmed with pink roses and gold bows;
Issued:	1999 in a limited edition of 2,000
Series:	1. Cinderella
	2. Fairy Tale Collection

PRICING DATA

U.S.	$ —
Can.	$ —
U.K.	£195.00

CINDERELLA'S SLIPPER

TECHNICAL DATA

Designer:	Sue McGarrigle
Modeller:	Jenny Oliver
Length:	3 ¼", 8.3 cm
Colour:	Ivory mother-of-pearl lustre; pink roses, green leaves on toe of shoe; black and gold clock on back of shoe; brown edging
Issued:	1999 to the present
Series:	1. Cinderella
	2. Precious Collections - Shoes

PRICING DATA

U.S.	$ —
Can.	$ —
U.K.	£39.00

CINDERELLA

PLATE

TECHNICAL DATA

Designer:	Sue McGarrigle
Diameter:	8", 25 cm
Colour:	Cinderella wears a white gown trimmed with pink roses; grey castle; pink rose bushes
Issued:	1999 to the present
Series:	1. Cinderella
	2. Fairy Tale Collection

PRICING DATA

U.S.	$ —
Can.	$ —
U.K.	£25.00

PRINCE CHARMING

TECHNICAL DATA

Designer:	Sue McGarrigle
Modeller:	Jack Glynn
Height:	10", 25.4 cm
Colour:	Dark brown coat with gold trim; apricot pantaloons and sash with gold trim; white cravat, cuffs and slipper; dark brown shoes with gold buckles
Issued:	2000 in a limited edition of 2,000
Series:	1. Cinderella
	2. Fairy Tale Collection

PRICING DATA

U.S.	$ —
Can.	$ —
U.K.	£195.00

PUMPKIN

TECHNICAL DATA

Designer:	Sue McGarrigle
Modeller:	Jenny Oliver
Height:	3 ½", 8.9 cm
Colour:	Orange pumpkin; green leaves; white mice
Issued:	1999 to the present

PRICING DATA

U.S.	$ —
Can.	$ —
U.K.	£49.00

LITTLE GREY RABBIT

First published in the late 1920s, by Alison Uttley, the books on the 'Little Grey Rabbit' numbered over 35. These books were illustrated by Margaret Tempest.

BIRTHDAY

TECHNICAL DATA

Designer:	Margaret Tempest
Modeller:	Catherine Barnsley
Height:	4", 10.1 cm
Colour:	Grey dress; pale blue apron; white tablecloth and cake; yellow candles
Issued:	1981-1982

PRICING DATA

U.S.	$30.00
Can.	$45.00
U.K.	£20.00

CHRISTMAS

TECHNICAL DATA

Designer:	Margaret Tempest
Modeller:	Catherine Barnsley
Height:	3 ½", 8.9 cm
Colour:	Grey dress; blue cape; brown basket; green, blue, red and yellow gift boxes
Issued:	1981-1982

PRICING DATA

U.S.	$45.00
Can.	$65.00
U.K.	£30.00

DIARY

TECHNICAL DATA

Designer:	Margaret Tempest
Modeller:	Catherine Barnsley
Height:	4", 10.1 cm
Colour:	Grey dress; brown desk; white and brown stool
Issued:	1978-1982

PRICING DATA

U.S.	$30.00
Can.	$45.00
U.K.	£20.00

LITTLE GREY RABBIT

FUZZYPEG

TECHNICAL DATA

Designer:	Margaret Tempest
Modeller:	Alan Harmer
Height:	2 ¾", 7.0 cm
Colour:	Grey jacket; rose-pink scarf; pale blue ball
Issued:	1981-1982

PRICING DATA

U.S.	$30.00
Can.	$45.00
U.K.	£20.00

GOES SHOPPING

TECHNICAL DATA

Designer:	Margaret Tempest
Modeller:	Catherine Barnsley
Height:	4", 10.1 cm
Colour:	Grey dress; blue cape; brown basket
Issued:	1978-1982

PRICING DATA

U.S.	$30.00
Can.	$45.00
U.K.	£20.00

HARE

TECHNICAL DATA

Designer:	Margaret Tempest
Modeller:	Alan Harmer
Height:	4 ¼", 10.8 cm
Colour:	Dark blue jacket; white shirt; yellow tie; grey waistcoat with red buttons; brown basket
Issued:	1978-1982

PRICING DATA

U.S.	$40.00
Can.	$60.00
U.K.	£25.00

LITTLE GREY RABBIT

LITTLE GREY RABBIT

TECHNICAL DATA

Designer:	Margaret Tempest
Modeller:	Catherine Barnsley
Height:	4", 10.1 cm
Colour:	Grey dress; pale blue pinafore
Issued:	1978-1982

PRICING DATA

U.S.	$30.00
Can.	$45.00
U.K.	£20.00

MOLDY WARP

TECHNICAL DATA

Designer:	Margaret Tempest
Modeller:	Alan Harmer
Height:	2 ½", 6.4 cm
Colour:	Brown mole; russet and yellow waistcoat; lilac sleeves and scarf
Issued:	1978-1982

PRICING DATA

U.S.	$40.00
Can.	$60.00
U.K.	£25.00

SPECKLEDY HEN

TECHNICAL DATA

Designer:	Margaret Tempest
Modeller:	Catherine Barnsley
Height:	3 ¼", 8.3 cm
Colour:	Brown hen; green bonnet and apron; yellow chicks
Issued:	1978-1982

PRICING DATA

U.S.	$40.00
Can.	$60.00
U.K.	£25.00

LITTLE GREY RABBIT

SQUIRREL

TECHNICAL DATA

Designer:	Margaret Tempest
Modeller:	Catherine Barnsley
Height:	3", 7.6 cm
Colour:	Brown squirrel; yellow dress; green collar and cuffs; lilac knitting
Issued:	1978-1982

PRICING DATA

U.S.	$30.00
Can.	$45.00
U.K.	£20.00

WASHDAY

TECHNICAL DATA

Designer:	Margaret Tempest
Modeller:	Catherine Barnsley
Height:	3", 7.6 cm
Colour:	Grey dress; blue washing; brown tub
Issued:	1978-1982

PRICING DATA

U.S.	$40.00
Can.	$60.00
U.K.	£25.00

WATER RAT

TECHNICAL DATA

Designer:	Margaret Tempest
Modeller:	Catherine Barnsley
Height:	3 ¼", 8.3 cm
Colour:	Brown water rat; green jacket with yellow collar, pockets and buttons
Issued:	1978-1982

PRICING DATA

U.S.	$40.00
Can.	$60.00
U.K.	£25.00

PADDINGTON BEAR

AND THE CAKES

TECHNICAL DATA

Modeller:	Catherine Barnsley
Height:	3 ¾", 9.5 cm
Colour:	1. Blue duffle coat; black hat with yellow band; white plate of cakes
	2. Blue duffle coat; green hat with yellow band; white plate of cakes
Issued:	1983-1985

PRICING DATA

U.S.	$85.00
Can.	$125.00
U.K.	£55.00

AUNT LUCY

TECHNICAL DATA

Modeller:	Catherine Barnsley
Height:	4", 10.1 cm
Colour:	Yellow and brown coat and shawl; black hat with pale brown band; black shoes
Issued:	1981-1985

PRICING DATA

U.S.	$100.00
Can.	$150.00
U.K.	£70.00

ARTIST
First Version

TECHNICAL DATA

Modeller:	Margaret Whitaker
Height:	5", 12.7 cm
Colour:	Blue duffle coat; black hat with yellow band; white scarf with red polka dots; white palette of paint; brown paint brush
Issued:	1976-1988

PRICING DATA

U.S.	$125.00
Can.	$175.00
U.K.	£85.00

PADDINGTON BEAR

ARTIST
Second Version

TECHNICAL DATA

Modeller:	Catherine Barnsley
Height:	3 ¾", 9.5 cm
Colour:	Green duffle coat; black hat with yellow band; white scarf with red polka dots; white palette of paint; brown paint brush and easel
Issued:	1981-1985

PRICING DATA

U.S.	$85.00
Can.	$125.00
U.K.	£60.00

AT THE SEASIDE

TECHNICAL DATA

Modeller:	Margaret Whitaker
Height:	3", 7.6 cm
Colour:	Yellow bear; blue swimming trunks; black hat with yellow band; brown sunglasses
Issued:	1976-1988

PRICING DATA

U.S.	$75.00
Can.	$110.00
U.K.	£50.00

BAKES A CAKE
First Verson

TECHNICAL DATA

Modeller:	Margaret Whitaker
Height:	5", 12.7 cm
Colour:	Blue coat; white apron and bowl; black hat with yellow band
Issued:	1976-1988

PRICING DATA

U.S.	$125.00
Can.	$175.00
U.K.	£85.00

PADDINGTON BEAR

BAKES A CAKE
Second Version

TECHNICAL DATA

Modeller:	Catherine Barnsley
Height:	3 ½", 8.9 cm
Colour:	Blue jacket; white apron and bowl; black hat with yellow band
Issued:	1981-1988
Series:	Miniatures

PRICING DATA

U.S.	$75.00
Can.	$110.00
U.K.	£50.00

BALLET DANCER

TECHNICAL DATA

Modeller:	Catherine Barnsley
Height:	4", 10.1 cm
Colour:	Yellow bear; white tutu; black hat with yellow band
Issued:	1983-1985

PRICING DATA

U.S.	$85.00
Can.	$125.00
U.K.	£60.00

BATH TIME
First Version

TECHNICAL DATA

Modeller:	Margaret Whitaker
Height:	4 ½", 11.9 cm
Colour:	White towel with blue fringe; green cap
Issued:	1976-1988

PRICING DATA

U.S.	$125.00
Can.	$175.00
U.K.	£85.00

PADDINGTON BEAR

BATH TIME
Second Version

TECHNICAL DATA

Modeller:	Catherine Barnsley
Height:	3 ½", 5.9 cm
Colour:	White towel with blue fringe; green cap
Issued:	1981-1988
Series:	Miniatures

PRICING DATA

U.S.	$85.00
Can.	$125.00
U.K.	£60.00

BIRTHDAY PARTY

TECHNICAL DATA

Modeller:	Margaret Whitaker
Height:	3 ½", 8.9 cm
Colour:	Blue duffle coat; white party hat and cracker
Issued:	1976-1980

PRICING DATA

U.S.	$75.00
Can.	$110.00
U.K.	£50.00

CHIMNEY SWEEP
First Version

TECHNICAL DATA

Modeller:	Margaret Whitaker
Height:	5", 12.7 cm
Colour:	Blue coat; black hat with yellow band; brown brushes and sack
Issued:	1976-1988

PRICING DATA

U.S.	$125.00
Can.	$175.00
U.K.	£85.00

PADDINGTON BEAR

CHIMNEY SWEEP
Second Version

TECHNICAL DATA

Modeller:	Catherine Barnsley
Height:	3 ½", 8.9 cm
Colour:	Brown coat; black hat with yellow band; brown brushes and sack
Issued:	1981-1985

PRICING DATA

U.S.	$75.00
Can.	$110.00
U.K.	£50.00

THE DECORATOR

TECHNICAL DATA

Modeller:	Catherine Barnsley
Height:	3 ½", 8.9 cm
Colour:	Blue jacket; black hat with yellow band; red bucket; brown, yellow and white paint brush
Issued:	1983-1988
Series:	Miniatures

PRICING DATA

U.S.	$75.00
Can.	$110.00
U.K.	£50.00

GOES FISHING

TECHNICAL DATA

Modeller:	Catherine Barnsley
Height:	3", 7.6 cm
Colour:	Green duffle coat; black hat with yellow band; brown fishing pole
Issued:	1981-1985

PRICING DATA

U.S.	$75.00
Can.	$110.00
U.K.	£50.00

PADDINGTON BEAR

GOES SKIING

TECHNICAL DATA

Modeller:	Catherine Barnsley
Height:	3 ¾", 9.5 cm
Colour:	1. Blue coat; red trousers; black hat with yellow band; brown skis and ski poles
	2. Yellow duffle coat; green hat with yellow band; green trousers; brown skis, ski poles
Issued:	1. 1983-1988
	2. 1981-1985

PRICING DATA

U.S.	$75.00
Can.	$110.00
U.K.	£50.00

GOES SLEDGING

TECHNICAL DATA

Modeller:	Catherine Barnsley
Height:	3", 7.6 cm
Colour:	Blue duffle coat; red hat with yellow band; white scarf with pink dots; yellow boots and goggles
Issued:	1983-1988
Variation:	Tobogganing

PRICING DATA

U.S.	$75.00
Can.	$110.00
U.K.	£50.00

HAS A NAP

TECHNICAL DATA

Modeller:	Catherine Barnsley
Height:	3", 7.6 cm
Colour:	1. Blue coat; black hat with yellow band; brown chair, book
	2. Blue coat; red hat with yellow band; brown chair, book
Issued:	1983-1988

PRICING DATA

U.S.	$75.00
Can.	$110.00
U.K.	£50.00

PADDINGTON BEAR

HITCHES A LIFT, First Version

TECHNICAL DATA

Modeller:	Margaret Whitaker
Height:	4 ½", 11.9 cm
Colour:	Blue duffle coat; black hat with yellow band; brown case
Issued:	1976-1988

PRICING DATA

U.S.	$125.00
Can.	$175.00
U.K.	£85.00

HITCHES A LIFT, Second Version

TECHNICAL DATA

Modeller:	Catherine Barnsley
Height:	2 ¾", 7.0 cm
Colour:	1. Blue duffle coat; black hat with yellow band; brown case
	2. Green duffle coat; blue hat with yellow band; brown case
Issued:	1981-1988
Series:	Miniatures

PRICING DATA

U.S.	$65.00
Can.	$100.00
U.K.	£45.00

IN THE SNOW, First Version

TECHNICAL DATA

Modeller:	Margaret Whitaker
Height:	4 ½", 11.9 cm
Colour:	Blue duffle coat; black hat with yellow band; white scarf with red polka dots; red wellington boots; white snowballs
Issued:	1976-1988

PRICING DATA

U.S.	$100.00
Can.	$150.00
U.K.	£70.00

PADDINGTON BEAR

IN THE SNOW, Second Version

TECHNICAL DATA

Modeller:	Catherine Barnsley
Height:	4", 10.1 cm
Colour:	1. Blue duffle coat; black hat with yellow band; white scarf with red fringe and polka dots; red wellington boots
	2. Green duffle coat; red hat with yellow band; white scarf with blue fringe and polka dots; red wellington boots
Issued:	1981-1988
Series:	Miniatures

PRICING DATA

U.S.	$75.00
Can.	$110.00
U.K.	£50.00

MAGICIAN WITH RABBIT

TECHNICAL DATA

Modeller:	Margaret Whitaker
Height:	4 ¾", 12.1 cm
Colour:	White robe with coloured moons, stars and circles; black hat with yellow band; white wand; white rabbit in black top hat
Issued:	1976-1988

PRICING DATA

U.S.	$125.00
Can.	$175.00
U.K.	£85.00

MAGICIAN WITH WAND

TECHNICAL DATA

Modeller:	Catherine Barnsley
Height:	3 ½" 8.9 cm
Colour:	White robe with coloured moons, stars and circles; black hat with yellow band; black wand; black top hat
Issued:	1981-1988

PRICING DATA

U.S.	$125.00
Can.	$175.00
U.K.	£85.00

PADDINGTON BEAR

MARMALADE SANDWICH

TECHNICAL DATA

Modeller:	Catherine Barnsley
Height:	3", 7.6 cm
Colour:	1. Yellow bear; blue duffle coat; black hat with yellow band
	2. Brown bear; blue duffle coat; red hat with yellow band
Issued:	1981-1988

PRICING DATA

U.S.	$75.00
Can.	$110.00
U.K.	£50.00

ON THE BEACH

TECHNICAL DATA

Modeller:	Catherine Barnsley
Height:	3 ½", 5.9 cm
Colour:	Brown duffle coat; black hat with yellow band; yellow life saver; brown spade and bucket
Issued:	1981-1985

PRICING DATA

U.S.	$75.00
Can.	$110.00
U.K.	£50.00

PAPERS HIS ROOM

TECHNICAL DATA

Modeller:	Margaret Whitaker
Height:	5", 12.7 cm
Colour:	Blue duffle coat; black hat with yellow band; white wallpaper with red daisies; brown, yellow and black brush
Issued:	1976-1988

PRICING DATA

U.S.	$100.00
Can.	$150.00
U.K.	£70.00

PADDINGTON BEAR

READS A BOOK
First Version

TECHNICAL DATA

Modeller:	Margaret Whitaker
Height:	3 ¼", 8.3 cm
Colour:	White pyjamas with blue and red flowers; black hat with yellow band; white and brown book
Issued:	1976-1988

PRICING DATA

U.S.	$80.00
Can.	$120.00
U.K.	£55.00

READS A BOOK
Second Version

TECHNICAL DATA

Modeller:	Catherine Barnsley
Height:	2 ¾", 7.0 cm
Colour:	White pyjamas with blue and red flowers; black hat with yellow band white and brown book
Issued:	1981-1985
Series:	Miniatures

PRICING DATA

U.S.	$65.00
Can.	$100.00
U.K.	£45.00

SHOPPING
First Version

TECHNICAL DATA

Modeller:	Margaret Whitaker
Height:	4 ¾", 12.1 cm
Colour:	Blue duffle coat; black hat with yellow band; brown shopping cart
Issued:	1976-1988

PRICING DATA

U.S.	$125.00
Can.	$175.00
U.K.	£85.00

PADDINGTON BEAR

SHOPPING
Second Version

TECHNICAL DATA

Modeller:	Catherine Barnsley
Height:	3 ¾", 9.5 cm
Colour:	Dark brown duffle coat; black hat with yellow band; brown shopping cart
Issued:	1981-1988
Series:	Miniatures

PRICING DATA

U.S.	$100.00
Can.	$150.00
U.K.	£70.00

TAKES A SNACK
First Version

TECHNICAL DATA

Designer:	Unknown
Modeller:	Margaret Whitaker
Height:	4 ½", 11.9 cm
Colour:	Yellow bear; black hat with yellow band; white mug with blue stripes; dark blue pouffe; white base
Issued:	1976-1988

PRICING DATA

U.S.	$100.00
Can.	$150.00
U.K.	£70.00

TAKES A SNACK
Second Version

TECHNICAL DATA

Modeller:	Catherine Barnsley
Height:	3 ½", 8.9 cm
Colour:	Yellow bear; black hat with yellow band; white mug with blue stripes; pale blue pouffe
Issued:	1980-1985
Series:	Miniatures

PRICING DATA

U.S.	$75.00
Can.	$110.00
U.K.	£50.00

PADDINGTON BEAR

TAKES A WALK

TECHNICAL DATA

Modeller:	Catherine Barnsley
Height:	3 ¾", 9.5 cm
Colour:	1. Yellow bear; blue duffle coat; black hat with yellow band
	2. Brown bear; yellow duffle coat green hat with yellow band
Issued:	1983-1988

PRICING DATA

U.S.	$75.00
Can.	$110.00
U.K.	£50.00

TAKES IT EASY
First Version

TECHNICAL DATA

Modeller:	Margaret Whitaker
Height:	3 ½", 8.9 cm
Colour:	Yellow bear; black hat with yellow band; brown and white deckchair
Issued:	1976-1985

PRICING DATA

U.S.	$80.00
Can.	$120.00
U.K.	£55.00

TAKES IT EASY
Second Version

TECHNICAL DATA

Modeller:	Catherine Barnsley
Height:	2 ¾", 7.0 cm
Colour:	Yellow bear; black hat with yellow band; brown and white deckchair
Issued:	1976-1985
Series:	Miniatures

PRICING DATA

U.S.	$65.00
Can.	$100.00
U.K.	£45.00

PADDINGTON BEAR

TOBOGGANING

TECHNICAL DATA

Modeller:	Catherine Barnsley
Height:	3", 7.6 cm
Colour:	Blue duffle coat; white scarf with red polka dots and fringe; black hat with yellow band; red boots; brown toboggan and goggles
Issued:	1983-1988
Variation:	Goes Sledging

PRICING DATA

U.S.	$75.00
Can.	$110.00
U.K.	£50.00

WAITS FOR A TRAIN

TECHNICAL DATA

Modeller:	Margaret Whitaker
Height:	2 ¾", 7.0 cm
Colour:	1. Brown bear; blue coat; black hat with yellow band; brown case
	2. Yellow bear; dark green coat; black hat with yellow band; brown case
	3. Brown bear; light green coat; blue hat with yellow band; brown case
Issued:	1976-1988

PRICING DATA

U.S.	$65.00
Can.	$100.00
U.K.	£45.00

WITH APPLES, First Version

TECHNICAL DATA

Modeller:	Margaret Whitaker
Height:	2 ½", 6.4 cm
Colour:	Blue duffle coat; black hat with yellow band; rosy apples
Issued:	1976-1985

PRICING DATA

U.S.	$75.00
Can.	$110.00
U.K.	£50.00

PADDINGTON BEAR

WITH APPLES
Second Version

TECHNICAL DATA

Modeller:	Catherine Barnsley
Height:	2 ¾", 7.0 cm
Colour:	Brown duffle coat; black hat with yellow band; rosy apples
Issued:	1976-1985

PRICING DATA

U.S.	$75.00
Can.	$110.00
U.K.	£50.00

WITH BIG DRUM

TECHNICAL DATA

Modeller:	Catherine Barnsley
Height:	3 ½", 8.9 cm
Colour:	Blue duffle coat; black hat with yellow band; beige, cream and brown drum
Issued:	1981-1985

PRICING DATA

U.S.	$85.00
Can.	$125.00
U.K.	£60.00

WITH MARMALADE

TECHNICAL DATA

Designer:	Unknown
Modeller:	Margaret Whitaker
Height:	4 ½", 11.9 cm
Colour:	White pyjamas with blue and red flowers; black hat with yellow band; yellow marmalade jar
Issued:	1976-1988

PRICING DATA

U.S.	$100.00
Can.	$150.00
U.K.	£70.00

PADDINGTON BEAR BROOCHES

At the Seaside
The Decorator
The Gardener
Goes Skiing
Marmalade
Plays Tennis

TECHNICAL DATA

Modeller:	Unknown
Height:	Unknown
Colour:	Blue, yellow and black
Issued:	Unknown

PRICING DATA

U.S.	$75.00
Can.	$100.00
U.K.	£50.00

Note: The Paddington Bear brooches are displayed in the box of issue, and are priced individually.

PADDINGTON BEAR LAMP BASE

"PADDINGTON WAITS FOR A TRAIN"

TECHNICAL DATA

Modeller:	Margaret Whitaker
Height:	7 ½", 19.1 cm
Colour:	Light brown lamp base; yellow bear wearing a blue duffle coat; black hat with yellow band; brown case; yellow jar of marmalade
Issued:	1976-1988

PRICING DATA

U.S.	$150.00
Can.	$225.00
U.K.	£100.00

PADDINGTON BEAR MONEY BOX

TECHNICAL DATA

Modeller:	Unknown
Height:	3", 7.6 cm
Colour:	White money box with four Paddington Bear designs; "Paddington wasn't the sort of bear who believed in taking chances."
Issued:	Unknown

PRICING DATA

U.S.	$25.00
Can.	$40.00
U.K.	£15.00

POSTMAN PAT

FATHER CHRISTMAS

TECHNICAL DATA

Designer:	Unknown
Modeller:	Unknown
Height:	3 ¼", 8.3 cm
Colour:	Dark green jacket; red hat with white trim; red scarf; green parcel; black and white cat
Issued:	1985-1987

PRICING DATA

U.S.	$150.00
Can.	$225.00
U.K.	£100.00

GRANNY DRYDEN

TECHNICAL DATA

Designer:	Unknown
Modeller:	Unknown
Height:	3 ¼", 8.3 cm
Colour:	Pink cardigan; brown dress; grey hair and spectacles; black shoes
Issued:	1985-1987

PRICING DATA

U.S.	$150.00
Can.	$225.00
U.K.	£100.00

JESS THE CAT

TECHNICAL DATA

Designer:	Unknown
Modeller:	Unknown
Height:	2 ¾", 7.0 cm
Colour:	Black cat; brown parcel
Issued:	1985-1987

PRICING DATA

U.S.	$150.00
Can.	$225.00
U.K.	£100.00

POSTMAN PAT

MISS HUBARD

TECHNICAL DATA

Designer:	Unknown
Modeller:	Unknown
Height:	3 ¾", 9.5 cm
Colour:	Red skirt and jacket; yellow collar; white blouse
Issued:	1985-1987

PRICING DATA

U.S.	$150.00
Can.	$225.00
U.K.	£100.00

MRS GOGGINS

TECHNICAL DATA

Designer:	Unknown
Modeller:	Unknown
Height:	3 ¼", 8.3 cm
Colour:	Black dress with red flowers; white apron; red shawl; grey hair
Issued:	1985-1987

PRICING DATA

U.S.	$150.00
Can.	$225.00
U.K.	£100.00

PETER FOGG

TECHNICAL DATA

Designer:	Unknown
Modeller:	Unknown
Height:	3 ½", 8.9 cm
Colour:	Brown jacket and trousers; orange pullover
Issued:	1985-1987

PRICING DATA

U.S.	$150.00
Can.	$225.00
U.K.	£100.00

POSTMAN PAT

POSTMAN PAT

TECHNICAL DATA

Designer:	Unknown
Modeller:	Unknown
Height:	3 ¾", 9.5 cm
Colour:	Dark green jacket, trousers and cap; brown sack and parcel
Issued:	1985-1987

PRICING DATA

U.S.	$150.00
Can.	$225.00
U.K.	£100.00

POSTMAN PAT WITH JESS

TECHNICAL DATA

Designer:	Unknown
Modeller:	Unknown
Height:	3 ¼", 8.3 cm
Colour:	Dark green jacket, trousers and cap; black and white cat
Issued:	1986-1987

PRICING DATA

U.S.	$150.00
Can.	$225.00
U.K.	£100.00

REVEREND TIMMS

TECHNICAL DATA

Designer:	Unknown
Modeller:	Unknown
Height:	3 ½", 8.9 cm
Colour:	Grey suit with black buttons; black shoes; white hair
Issued:	1985-1987

PRICING DATA

U.S.	$150.00
Can.	$225.00
U.K.	£100.00

POSTMAN PAT

SCARECROW PAT

TECHNICAL DATA

Designer:	Unknown
Modeller:	Unknown
Height:	3 ¼", 8.3 cm
Colour:	Brown hat and coat; orange scarf; black bird
Issued:	1985-1987

PRICING DATA

U.S.	$150.00
Can.	$225.00
U.K.	£100.00

POSTMAN PAT MONEY BOX

TECHNICAL DATA

Designer:	Unknown
Modeller:	Unknown
Height:	3", 7.6 cm
Colour:	White; blue, black, green and red
Issued:	1985-1987

PRICING DATA

U.S.	$80.00
Can.	$120.00
U.K.	£55.00

SLEEPING BEAUTY

ENCHANTED CASTLE

TECHNICAL DATA

Designer:	Charlotte Royal
Modeller:	Jenny Oliver
Height:	4", 10.1 cm
Colour:	White; red-brown roof; beige door; green grass
Issued:	2000 to the present
Series:	Sleeping Beauty

PRICING DATA

U.S.	$ —
Can.	$ —
U.K.	£39.00

PLATE

TECHNICAL DATA

Designer:	Sue McGarrigle
Height:	8", 20.3 cm
Colour:	Sleeping Beauty: Maroon dress Wicked Witch: Yellow dress; black cloak wih yellow lining; pale brown spinning wheel
Issued:	2000 to the present
Series:	1. Fairy Tale Collection
	2. Sleeping Beauty

PRICING DATA

U.S.	$ —
Can.	$ —
U.K.	£25.00

SLEEPING BEAUTY

SLEEPING BEAUTY

TECHNICAL DATA

Designer:	Sue McGarrigle
Modeller:	Jack Glynn
Height:	5 ¾", 14.6 cm
Colour:	Maroon dress with gold trim; brown hair
Issued:	2000 in a limited edition of 2,000
Series:	1. Fairy Tale Collection
	2. Sleeping Beauty

PRICING DATA

U.S.	$ —
Can.	$ —
U.K.	£200.00

SLEEPING BEAUTY'S SHOE

TECHNICAL DATA

Designer:	Sue McGarrigle
Modeller:	Jenny Oliver
Height:	3 ½", 8.9 cm
Colour:	Rose-pink shoe decorated with pink roses, green leaves and gold trim; pink heel with rose-pink trim
Issued:	1999 to the present
Series:	1. Sleeping Beauty
	2. Precious Collection - Shoes

PRICING DATA

U.S.	$ —
Can.	$ —
U.K.	£39.00

RED HOUSE

COALPORT COLLECTOR SOCIETY

The international society for connoisseur's of fine china

Membership of this exclusive international society offers privileges no connoisseur of fine china should be without.

The beautiful products created by Coalport represent over two hundred years of fine china tradition and stand among the finest examples of the art anywhere in the world - precious collections lovingly crafted and decorated by hand, treasured by the most discerning.

By joining thousands of fellow enthusiasts who are already members of the Coalport Collector Society, you will be able to take advantage of many exclusive privileges.

THE PRIVILEGES AVAILABLE TO YOU

Free Debutante
A charming figurine is our special gift to you when you join the Coalport Collector Society.

Collector Magazine
You will be sent the authoritative Collector magazine every quarter. Packed with information, this 32-page publication includes previews of new products, competitions and special offers to help you get the most from your membership.

Exclusive Members-only Offers
Enjoy the opportunity to purchase precious collections produced by Coalport ONLY for Society Members, including The Modern Bride Collection and our exclusive figurine for the year.

Personalised Membership Card
This embossed Membership Card is your passport to all the privileges - yours by right as a Society Member.

Advance Notice of Figurine Painting Events
Ensure you don't miss an opportunity to meet Alf Willis or one of his colleagues demonstrate the art of hand painting.

Exclusive V.I.P. Factory Visits
Come to 'The Potteries' - home of Coalport - and be our guest for the day. Enjoy a complimentary lunch in our Visitor Centre before going on an exclusive tour around the Coalport factory to see how these beautiful products are 'brought to life'.

Entry to Wedgwood Visitor Centre
As a member, you will be able to bring your whole family - as many times as you like - to Wedgwood's Visitor Centre and Museum at Barlaston absolutely free (based on two adults and two children under 16 on each occasion).

20% off the entry price at the Coalport China Museum, Ironbridge
This offer, exclusive to Society members, may be used for entry into the Coalport China Museum at Ironbridge, or against any category of 'passport ticket', which admits to all the museums at Ironbridge Gorge.

Rewarding Your Loyalty
When you have spent £500 on Coalport products we will send you a £50 voucher that you can use in part payment for future purchases... with further benefits the longer you're a Member.
(UK and Canadian members only.)

Join today, or give Membership as a gift to somebody very special, for just £25/C$40

Please complete this form and return to:
Coalport Collector Society, PO Box 99, Sudbury, Suffolk CO10 6SN

For Canada:
Waterford Wedgwood Canada, 20 West Beaver Creek Road, Richmond Hill, Ontario L4B 3L6

A society for lovers of fine china

Personal Membership Application Form

The Coalport Collectors Society is open to anyone aged 18 or over. Please allow 28 days for delivery of your Membership Pack.
Please enrol me / my friend or relative as a Coalport Collector for one year at a cost of:

UK Residents £25 ☐ Canada Residents C$40 ☐ Overseas US$50 ☐ **Please complete all details in ink and CAPITAL LETTERS**

(Panel A)

Title (Mr/Mrs/Ms) _____ Sex: Male ☐ Female ☐ First Name _____ Second Initial _____

Last Name _____ Date of birth ☐☐ ☐☐ ☐☐

Address _____

Town/City _____ Postcode _____

Country _____ Tel area code _____ Tel No. _____

How would you like your name to appear on your Membership Card? (Maximum 25 characters including spacing)

☐☐☐☐☐☐☐☐☐☐☐☐☐☐☐☐☐☐☐☐☐☐☐☐☐

Preferred stockist (where you normally purchase your Coalport figurines):

Stockist's Name _____

Stockist's Address _____

For Gift Membership Only

Your friend or relative will be informed in their letter of welcome to the Society that their membership is a gift from you.
Please write in CAPITAL LETTERS your name as you wish it to appear on their letter of welcome.

Please enrol my friend/relative named below as a COALPORT COLLECTOR. I confirm that he/she is aged 18 or over.

Title (Mr/Mrs/Ms) _____ Sex: Male ☐ Female ☐ First Name _____ Second Initial _____

Last Name _____ Date of birth ☐☐ ☐☐ ☐☐

(Panel B)
ADDRESS OF GIFT MEMBERSHIP RECIPIENT (Must be completed in all cases)

Address _____

Town/City _____ Postcode _____ Country _____ Tel area code _____ Tel No. _____

How would you like member's name to appear on the Membership Card? (Maximum 25 characters including spacing)

☐☐☐☐☐☐☐☐☐☐☐☐☐☐☐☐☐☐☐☐☐☐☐☐☐

Please indicate if you wish the Gift Membership to be sent to your nominated recipient or to you so you can present the gift personally. Tick one:

☐ Please send the membership pack with my compliments direct to my friend or relative at the address in Panel B.

☐ I prefer to present the membership pack to my friend/relative personally; please send it in the first instance to me at the address in Panel A.

Method of Payment

I wish that I and/or my nominated friend/relative be enrolled in the Coalport Collector Society for the period of one year. I understand that membership costs **£25 (UK)/ C$40 (Canada)/US$50 (Overseas)** per person per year and is open to anyone aged 18 or over. I wish to pay by Cheque/Postal Order/Credit Card/Direct Debit/Switch, as shown below. **Please make Cheques/Postal Orders payable to Coalport Collector (in Canada to Waterford Wedgwood Canada).** Only payment by Credit Card can be accepted from overseas subscribers. (Canada members can also pay by cheque)
Tick one:

☐ I enclose a Cheque/Postal Order for £/C$ _____ for _____ memberships made payable to **Coalport Collector** (in Canada to Waterford Wedgwood Canada). Please ensure your address is written on the back of all cheques.

☐ Please charge my Visa/Access/Mastercard/Switch with the sum of: £/C$/US$ _____ for _____ membership(s).

Card No. ☐☐☐☐ ☐☐☐☐ ☐☐☐☐ ☐☐☐☐ ☐☐☐☐

Expiry Date ☐☐ ☐☐ Name on Card _____ Switch Issue No. ☐☐

Signature _____ Date _____ Name and billing address of cardholder (if different from Panel A)

Mr/Mrs/Ms _____ Address _____

Postcode _____

The Wedgwood Group, which Coalport joined in 1967, may send you details of other ceramic and crystal products and may use your name and address for marketing research purposes. If you prefer that your details are not used in this way, please tick here. ☐